CHAPTERS 1-28

Glencoe Accounting

CONCEPTS/PROCEDURES/APPLICATIONS

FIRST-YEAR COURSE
THIRD EDITION

Donald J. Guerrieri
Norwin Senior High School
North Huntingdon, Pennsylvania

F. Barry Haber
Fayetteville State University
Fayetteville, North Carolina

William B. Hoyt
Wilton High School
Wilton, Connecticut

Robert E. Turner
McNeese State University
Lake Charles, Louisiana

GLENCOE
McGraw-Hill

New York, New York   Columbus, Ohio   Woodland Hills, California   Peoria, Illinois

Send all inquiries to:
Glencoe/McGraw-Hill
21600 Oxnard St., Suite 500
Woodland Hills, CA 91367-4906

ISBN 0-02-803620-4

Printed in the United States of America.

12 13 14 15 16   066   05 04 03 02 01

1 Accounting in a Private Enterprise Economy

Name _____

Date _____ Class _____

Total Points: 39   Student's Score _____

Part 1   Accounting Vocabulary (10 points)

Directions: Using terms from the following list, complete the sentences below. Write the letter of the term you have chosen in the space provided. The first statement has been completed for you.

A. accounting clerk   E. charter   I. partnership
B. accounting system   F. corporation   J. profit
C. capital   G. fiscal period   K. sole proprietorship
D. certified public accountant   H. loss

Answer

_____K_____ 0. A(n) __?__ has one owner.
_____ 1. The time period covered by an accounting report is called a(n) __?__ .
_____ 2. A(n) __?__ has at least two owners.
_____ 3. Money invested in a business by an owner is called __?__ .
_____ 4. The amount of money earned over and above the amount spent to keep a business operating is called __?__ .
_____ 5. Businesses that spend more than they receive operate at a(n) __?__ .
_____ 6. The legal permission that gives a corporation the right to operate is called a(n) __?__ .
_____ 7. A(n) __?__ is concerned with the process of recording and reporting financial information.
_____ 8. A business organization that is recognized by law to have a life of its own is a(n) __?__ .
_____ 9. A person who holds an entry-level job in accounting is called a(n) __?__ .
_____ 10. A person who provides accounting services to clients for a fee is a(n) __?__ .

Part 2   The Basis of an Accounting System (9 points)

Directions: In the space provided before each term, write the letter of the definition that matches that term. The first term has been completed as an example.

Answer

_____B_____   0. Private enterprise economy
_____   1. Business entity
_____   2. General bookkeeper
_____   3. EFTS
_____   4. Going concern
_____   5. Accounting
_____   6. Managerial accountant
_____   7. Manufacturing business
_____   8. Merchandising business
_____   9. Service business

A. A standard means of communicating financial information in a form that is clearly understood by all those interested in the operations and financial condition of a business
B. Allows people to freely produce the goods and services they choose and use their money as they wish
C. An accountant employed within a business who may determine product costs and prepare budgets
D. A business that buys finished products and resells them to individuals or other businesses
E. Exists independently from its owner's personal holdings
F. Assumption that a business will continue to operate in the future
G. A system to speedily transfer money from one account to another
H. One person employed by a small- or medium-sized business to keep the accounting records
I. A business that buys raw materials and transforms them into finished products through the use of labor and machinery
J. A business that operates to provide a needed service for a fee

Part 3 Influences on Accounting (10 points)

Directions: Using the following list of terms, complete the sentences below. Write the letter of your choice in the space provided. The first sentence has been completed as an example.

A. American Accounting Association
B. American Institute of Certified Public Accountants
C. Certificate in Management Accounting
D. Certified Public Accountants
E. Computer

F. Financial Accounting Standards Board
G. Internal Revenue Service
H. National Association of Accountants
I. National Council on Governmental Accounting
J. Not-for-Profit Organizations
K. Securities and Exchange Commission

Answer

___F___   0. *Statements of Financial Accounting Standards* and *Interpretations* are issued by the __?__ .

_____   1. Principles of accounting for state and local governments are developed and interpreted by the __?__ .

_____   2. Accountants who hold a license issued by the state to practice accounting are __?__ .

_____   3. Groups that provide services to the general public and do not operate to make money are called __?__ .

_____   4. The sale of stock certificates to the general public is regulated by the __?__ .

_____   5. An organization of accounting professors and certified public accountants that is concerned with developing accounting standards is the __?__ .

_____   6. A(n) __?__ does not allow an accountant to perform services for the general public.

_____   7. The collection of federal taxes, the enforcement of tax regulations, and the interpretation of tax laws are responsibilities of the __?__ .

_____   8. The __?__ is a professional association made up of CPAs.

_____   9. The organization concerned with accounting for management purposes is the __?__ .

_____   10. The __?__ performs routine recordkeeping tasks and prepares reports.

Part 4 Accounting Information (10 points)

Directions: Read each of the following statements to determine whether the statement is true or false. Write your answer in the space provided. The first statement has been completed as an example.

Answer

___False___   0. The use of computers has significantly altered the basic accounting system.

_____   1. One measure of success in attracting dollars is the amount of profit a business earns.

_____   2. Only businesses that do not earn a profit will have the economic resources to continue to operate.

_____   3. Not all businesses need money to start and maintain operations.

_____   4. A sole proprietorship is a business owned and operated by two persons.

_____   5. Money is needed to buy or to make products.

_____   6. The sole proprietorship is the oldest and most common form of business organization.

_____   7. The sole proprietorship is the most difficult type of business to start.

_____   8. The corporation is not required by law to obtain permission to operate.

_____   9. Accountants make choices and decisions about the design of accounting systems and prepare and explain financial reports.

_____   10. Service, merchandising, and manufacturing businesses are alike because each business combines capital with labor, has operating costs, and does not operate to make a profit.

Exercise 3-1, Page 55

Account Title	Account Classification	Increase Side	Decrease Side	Normal Balance
Cash in Bank	Asset	Debit	Credit	Debit
Accounts Receivable	Asset	Debit	Credit	Debit
Office Equipment	Asset	Debit	Credit	Debit
Delivery Van	Asset	Debit	Credit	Debit
Accounts Payable	Liability	Credit	Debit	Credit
A. Schultz, Capital	Owner's Equity	Credit	Debit	Credit

Exercise 3-2, Page 55

1. _____

2. _____

3. _____

4. _____

Exercise 3-3, Page 55

1. a. Asset Cash in bank increased. Increases in assets are recorded as debit.

   b. Asset Office Furniture decreased. Decreases in Office Furniture are recorded as credit

2. a. Asset Office equipment increased. Increases in assets are recorded as debit.

   b. Accounts payable increased. Increases in accounts Payable are recorded as credit.

3. a. Asset Cash in bank decreased. Decreases in assets are recorded as credit

   b. Accounts payable decreased. Decreases in accounts payable are recorded as debit.

1. <u>Cash in Bank</u>

Debit	Credit
$40000	
Bal.$40000	

<u>Norman Rocky, Capital</u>

Debit	Credit
	+$40000
	Bal$40000

2. <u>Boat</u>

$27000	
+$27000	
Bal$67000	

<u>Accounts Payable</u>

$27000	
	+$27000
	Bal $67000

3. <u>Fishing Equipment</u>

+$3750	
+$3750	
Bal.$70750	

<u>Norman Rocky, Capital</u>

	+$3750
	+$43750
	Bal$70750

4. <u>Cash in Bank</u>

	-$7500
+$32500	
Bal$63250	

<u>Fishing Equipment</u>

+$7500	
+$11250	
Bal$70750	

5. <u>Fishing Equipment</u>

	-$1200
+$10050	
Bal$69550	

<u>Accounts Receivable</u>

+$1200	
$1200	
Bal$70750	

Exercise 4-1, Page 78

Account Title	Account Classification	Increase Side	Decrease Side	Normal Balance
Cash in Bank	Asset	Debit	Credit	Debit
Accounts Receivable	Asset	Debit	Credit	Debit
Airplanes	Asset	Debit	Credit	Debit
Accounts Payable	Liability	Credit	Debit	Credit
Edward Palmer, Capital	Owner's Equity	Credit	Debit	Credit
Edward Palmer, withdrawals	Owner's Equity	Credit	Debit	Credit
Flying Fees	Revenue	Credit	Debit	Credit
Advertising Expense	Expense	Debit	Credit	Debit
Food Expense	Expense	Debit	Credit	Debit
Fuel & Oil Expense	Expense	Debit	Credit	Debit
Repairs Expense	Expense	Debit	Credit	Debit

Exercise 4-2, Page 78

1. Utilities Expense - debit, Cash in bank - credit
2. Accounts Receivable - debit, Service Fee - credit
3. Cash in bank - credit, John Albers, withdrawal - debit
4. Cash in bank - credit, Advertising expense - debit

Exercise 4-3, Page 78

1. a. _____
   _____
   b. _____
   _____
2. a. _____
   _____
   b. _____
   _____
3. a. _____
   _____
   b. _____

1.

Cash in Bank	
+	−
$1675	

Ligal Fus	
+	
	$1675

2.

Cash in Bank	
+	−
	$450

Rent Expense	
+	−
$450	

3.

Cash in Bank	
+	−
	$250

Esther Wills, Withdrawals	
+	−
$250	

4.

Accounts Payable	
+	−
$245	

Repairs Expense	
+	−
$245	

Problem 4-4, Page 80

Problem 4-4, Page 80 (Concluded)
(4)

Account Title	Debit Balances	Credit Balances
	$ _____	$ _____
	_____	_____
	_____	_____
	_____	_____
	_____	_____
	_____	_____
	_____	_____
	_____	_____
	_____	_____
	_____	_____
Totals	$ _____	$ _____

Problem 4-5, Page 81

	Assets	=	Liabilities	+	Owner's Equity	−	Withdrawals	+	Revenue	−	Expenses
1.	$ _____		$ 8,200		$56,300		$ 500		$10,000		$ 9,600
2.	$22,150		$ 525		$18,800		$ 1,200		$12,100		$ _____
3.	$17,500		$ 75		$21,650		$ _____		$ 4,115		$ 3,250
4.	$49,450		$ _____		$47,840		$ 1,500		$20,300		$17,610
5.	$21,900		$ 1,150		$20,005		$ 950		$ _____		$16,570
6.	$72,640		$ 2,790		$ _____		$10,750		$67,908		$39,749
7.	$ _____		$ 1,988		$41,194		$ 6,196		$52,210		$42,597
8.	$50,780		$ 1,493		$64,110		$16,050		$ _____		$29,986
9.	$ _____		$ 3,840		$61,774		$ _____		$40,163		$21,637

(Expenses plus withdrawals equal $27,749.)

	Assets	=	Liabilities	+	Owner's Equity	−	Withdrawals	+	Revenue	−	Expenses
10.	$64,070		$ _____		$49,102		$ 4,875		$53,166		$ _____

(Total owner's equity after adding revenue and subtracting expenses and withdrawals is $50,643.)

Exercise 5-1, Page 101

Trans.	Account Title	Account Classification	Account Increase	Account Decrease	General Journal Debit	General Journal Credit
1	Delivery Van	Asset	√		√	
	Cash in Bank	Asset		√		√
2	Utilities Expense	Expense	✓		✓	
	Cash in Bank	Asset		✓		✓
3	Cash in Bank	Asset	✓		✓	
	Day care Fees	Revenue	✓			✓
4	Patti Fair-Withdrawal	Owner's Equity	✓		✓	
	Cash in Bank	Asset		✓		✓
5	Accounts Receivable	Asset	✓		✓	
	Day Care Fees	Revenue	✓			✓
6	Office Furniture	Asset	✓		✓	
	Patti Fair - Capital	Owner's Equity	✓			✓

Exercise 5-2, Page 102

GENERAL JOURNAL   PAGE _12_

	DATE		DESCRIPTION	POST. REF.	DEBIT	CREDIT	
1	19-- July	2	~~Store Supplies~~ Office Supplies		100 00		1
2			Cash in Bank			100 00	2
3			Check 419				3
4		3	Cash in Bank		300 00		4
5			Accts. Rec. – Arc Company			300 00	5
6			Receipt 422				6

Exercise 5-3, Page 102

Location of Account	Account Number
1. The first asset account	101
2. First liability account	201
3. Owner's Equity account	301
4. First revenue account	401
5. First expense account	501
6. Owner's withdrawal account	305
7 Second asset account	105
8 Second expense account	510
9 Third asset account	110
10 Second liability account	205
11 Third expense account	520
12 Fourth asset account	120

Problem 5-1, Page 103

Exercise 6-1, Page 123

Trans. No.	Account Affected	Debit	Credit	Balance Debit	Balance Credit
1	Utilities Expense	✓		✓	
2	Alterations Revenue		✓		✓
3	Supplies	✓		✓	
4	Kati Karl, withdrawals	✓		✓	
5	Accounts Payable, ALCO Inc.	✓			✓
6	Accounts Receivable-A. Jones		✓	✓	

Exercise 6-2, Page 123

ACCOUNT _____ ACCOUNT NO. _____

DATE	EXPLANATION	POST. REF.	DEBIT	CREDIT	BALANCE DEBIT	BALANCE CREDIT

Exercise 6-3, Page 123

Error	Does Error Affect Trial Balance?	Correcting Entry Required?
1	Yes	No
2	No	Yes
3	No	Yes
4	Yes	Yes
5	Yes	No
6	Yes	No
7	Yes	No
8	Yes	N

Problem 6-1, Page 124

PAGE ___1___

	DATE	DESCRIPTION	POST. REF.	DEBIT	CREDIT	
1	19-- Sept. 1	Cash in Bank		1900 00		1
2		Giles Gilbert, Capital			1900 00	2
3		Memo. 1				3
4	3	Dental Supplies		330 00		4
5		Accts. Pay. - Dental Distributors			330 00	5
6		Invoice AB500				6
7	4	Dental Equipment		2700 00		7
8		Accts. Pay. - Dental Distributors			2700 00	8
9		Invoice AB580				9
10	6	Furniture and Fixtures		280 00		10
11		Giles Gilbert, Capital			280 00	11
12		Memo. 2				12
13	8	Cash in Bank		1200 00		13
14		Professional Fees			1200 00	14
15		Receipt 100				15
16	10	Accts. Pay. - Dental Distributors		330 00		16
17		Cash in Bank			330 00	17
18		Check 101				18
19	12	Accts. Rec. - Sarah Ashley		750 00		19
20		Professional Fees			750 00	20
21		Invoice 100				21
22	15	Giles Gilbert, Withdrawals		600 00		22
23		Cash in Bank			600 00	23
24		Check 102				24
25	19	Cash in Bank		1650 00		25
26		Professional Fees			1650 00	26
27		Receipt 101				27
28	28	Cash in Bank		375 00		28
29		Accts. Rec. - Sarah Ashley			375 00	29
30		Receipt 102				30
31	29	Accts. Rec. - Rod McCune		490 00		31
32		Professional Fees			490 00	32
33		Invoice 101				33
34	30	Utilities Expense		140 00		34
35		Cash in Bank			140 00	35
36		Check 103				36
37						37
38						38

Problem 6-4, Page 125 (Continued)

GENERAL LEDGER

ACCOUNT _____ ACCOUNT NO. _____

DATE	EXPLANATION	POST. REF.	DEBIT	CREDIT	BALANCE DEBIT	CREDIT

ACCOUNT _____ ACCOUNT NO. _____

DATE	EXPLANATION	POST. REF.	DEBIT	CREDIT	BALANCE DEBIT	CREDIT

ACCOUNT _____ ACCOUNT NO. _____

DATE	EXPLANATION	POST. REF.	DEBIT	CREDIT	BALANCE DEBIT	CREDIT

ACCOUNT _____ ACCOUNT NO. _____

DATE	EXPLANATION	POST. REF.	DEBIT	CREDIT	BALANCE DEBIT	CREDIT

ACCOUNT _____ ACCOUNT NO. _____

DATE	EXPLANATION	POST. REF.	DEBIT	CREDIT	BALANCE DEBIT	CREDIT

Problem 6-4, Page 125 (Continued)

ACCOUNT _____ ACCOUNT NO. _____

DATE	EXPLANATION	POST. REF.	DEBIT	CREDIT	BALANCE	
					DEBIT	CREDIT

ACCOUNT _____ ACCOUNT NO. _____

DATE	EXPLANATION	POST. REF.	DEBIT	CREDIT	BALANCE	
					DEBIT	CREDIT

ACCOUNT _____ ACCOUNT NO. _____

DATE	EXPLANATION	POST. REF.	DEBIT	CREDIT	BALANCE	
					DEBIT	CREDIT

ACCOUNT _____ ACCOUNT NO. _____

DATE	EXPLANATION	POST. REF.	DEBIT	CREDIT	BALANCE	
					DEBIT	CREDIT

ACCOUNT _____ ACCOUNT NO. _____

DATE	EXPLANATION	POST. REF.	DEBIT	CREDIT	BALANCE	
					DEBIT	CREDIT

ACCOUNT _____ ACCOUNT NO. _____

DATE	EXPLANATION	POST. REF.	DEBIT	CREDIT	BALANCE	
					DEBIT	CREDIT

Problem 6-4, Page 125 (Concluded)

Problem 6-5, Page 126

GENERAL JOURNAL

PAGE 21

	DATE		DESCRIPTION	POST. REF.	DEBIT	CREDIT	
1	19-- June	3	Furniture and Fixtures	125	1 25 00		1
2			Cash in Bank	101		1 25 00	2
3			Check 601				3
4		5	Cash in Bank	101	4 00 00		4
5			Accts. Rec. - James Brown	106		4 00 00	5
6			Receipt 302				6
7		7	Accts. Pay. - Vicki Dash		2 00 00		7
8			Cash in Bank	101		2 00 00	8
9			Check 602				9
10		9	Furniture and Fixtures	125	5 00 00		10
11			Cash in Bank	101		5 00 00	11
12			Check 603				12
13		13	Trina Lopez, Capital	301	1 20 0 00		13
14			Cash in Bank	101		1 20 0 00	14
15			Check 604				15
16		17	Cash in Bank	101	2 00 0 00		16
17			Trina Lopez, Capital	301		2 00 0 00	17
18			Receipt 303				18
19		19	Cash in Bank	101	75 00		19
20			Accts. Rec. - Suzanne Sharpe	110		75 00	20
21			Receipt 304				21
22		20	Cash in Bank	101	1 00 00		22
23			Accts. Rec. - James Brown	106		1 00 00	23
24			Receipt 305				24
25		24	Utilities Expense	520	75 00		25
26			Cash in Bank	101		75 00	26
27			Check 605				27
28		27	Cash in Bank	101	3 00 0 00		28
29			Trina Lopez, Withdrawals	305		3 00 0 00	29
30			Memo: 40				30
31		29	Cash in Bank	101	1 00 0 00		31
32			Professional Fees	401		1 00 0 00	32
33			Receipt 306				33
34							34
35							35
36							36
37							37
38							38

Problem 6-5, Page 126 (Continued)

GENERAL JOURNAL

PAGE _____

	DATE	DESCRIPTION	POST. REF.	DEBIT	CREDIT	
1						1
2						2
3						3
4						4
5						5
6						6
7						7
8						8
9						9
10						10
11						11
12						12
13						13
14						14
15						15
16						16
17						17
18						18
19						19

GENERAL LEDGER (PARTIAL)

ACCOUNT *Accounts Receivable – Suzanne Sharpe*   ACCOUNT NO. *110*

DATE		EXPLANATION	POST. REF.	DEBIT	CREDIT	BALANCE DEBIT	BALANCE CREDIT
19-- June	1	Balance	✓			300 00	
	19		G21		57 00	243 00	

ACCOUNT *Store Supplies*   ACCOUNT NO. *120*

DATE		EXPLANATION	POST. REF.	DEBIT	CREDIT	BALANCE DEBIT	BALANCE CREDIT
19-- June	1	Balance	✓			120 00	

ACCOUNT _Furniture and Fixtures_   ACCOUNT NO. _125_

DATE		EXPLANATION	POST. REF.	DEBIT	CREDIT	BALANCE DEBIT	BALANCE CREDIT
19-- June	1	Balance	✓			1 500 00	
	3		G21	1 25 00		1 625 00	
	9		G21	4 00 00		2 025 00	

ACCOUNT _Accounts Payable – Vicki Dash_   ACCOUNT NO. _204_

DATE		EXPLANATION	POST. REF.	DEBIT	CREDIT	BALANCE DEBIT	BALANCE CREDIT
19-- June	1	Balance	✓				2 200 00

ACCOUNT _Irina Lopez, Capital_   ACCOUNT NO. _301_

DATE		EXPLANATION	POST. REF.	DEBIT	CREDIT	BALANCE DEBIT	BALANCE CREDIT
19-- June	1	Balance	✓				13 000 00
	13		G21	1 200 00			11 800 00
	17		G21		2 000 00		13 800 00

ACCOUNT _Irina Lopez, Withdrawals_   ACCOUNT NO. _305_

DATE		EXPLANATION	POST. REF.	DEBIT	CREDIT	BALANCE DEBIT	BALANCE CREDIT
19-- June	1	Balance	✓			6 000 00	
	27		G21		3 000 00	3 000 00	

ACCOUNT _Professional Fees_   ACCOUNT NO. _401_

DATE		EXPLANATION	POST. REF.	DEBIT	CREDIT	BALANCE DEBIT	BALANCE CREDIT
19-- June	1	Balance	✓				10 000 00
	29		G21		1 000 00		11 000 00

Name _____ Date _____ Class _____

A-1 Computer Repair Co.
Work Sheet
For the Month Ended September 30, 19--

ACCT. NO.	ACCOUNT NAME	TRIAL BALANCE DEBIT	TRIAL BALANCE CREDIT	INCOME STATEMENT DEBIT	INCOME STATEMENT CREDIT	BALANCE SHEET DEBIT	BALANCE SHEET CREDIT
101	Cash in Bank	4728 00				4728 00	
105	Accts. Rec. - Sell Corp.	741 00				741 00	
110	Accts. Rec. - M+R Associates	1302 00				1320 00	
115	Office Furniture	3186 00				3186 00	
120	Computer Equipment	12963 00				12963 00	
125	Office Equipment	2859 00					
205	Accts. Pay. - Henry Crawford		5844 00				5844 00
210	Accts. Pay. - Alice Santos		2108 00				2108 00
215	Accts. Pay. - Mike Olson		317 00				3170 00
301	Lynn Austin, Capital		12485 00				12485 00
305	Lynn Austin, Withdrawals	2000 00		2000 00			
310	Income Summary						
401	Service Revenue		13742 00		13742 00		
501	Advertising Expense	2104 00		2104 00			
506	Entertainment Expense	578 00		587 00			
509	Miscellaneous Expense	492 00		492 00			
514	Rent Expense	2800 00		2800 00			
520	Utilities Expense	763 00			763 00		
		34516 00	34516 00				

Matt's Cleaning Service
Work Sheet
For the Month Ended March 31, 19—

	ACCT. NO.	ACCOUNT NAME	TRIAL BALANCE DEBIT	TRIAL BALANCE CREDIT	INCOME STATEMENT DEBIT	INCOME STATEMENT CREDIT	BALANCE SHEET DEBIT	BALANCE SHEET CREDIT
1	101	Cash in Bank	14862 40				14862 40	
2	105	Accts. Rec.–Lynn Jarok	2711 91				2711 91	
3	110	Accts. Rec.–Jeffrey Holden					1604 00	
4	115	Office Furniture	9881 40					
5	120	Office Equipment					3017 45	
6	125	Computer Equipment						
7	130	Delivery Equipment					9146 50	
8	201	Accts. Pay.–Peterson Supply		6013 19				6013 19
9	205	Accts. Pay.–Atlas Co.						
10	210	Accts. Pay.–New Mark, Inc.		5683 09				5683 09
11	301	Jason Stone, Capital						32450 00
12	305	Jason Stone, Withdrawals	2000 00					
13	310	Income Summary			—	—		
14	401	Commissions Revenue		14319 80		14319 80		
15	501	Advertising Expense	3605 00		3605 00			
16	505	Entertainment Expense			394 91			
17	510	Maintenance Expense			1831 40			
18	515	Miscellaneous Expense	432 65					
19	520	Rent Expense			5000 00			
20	525	Utilities Expense	213 24		213 24			
21								
22		Net Income			2842 60			
23								51081 45
24								
25								
26								

Exercise 8-1, Page 162

Account Title	Account Classification	Trial Balance		Financial Statements	
		Debit	Credit	Income Statement	Balance Sheet
Accts. Pay. — Boyden Co.	Liability		✓		✓
Accts. Pay. — Gail's Supplies	Liability		✓		✓
Accts. Rec. — Clinton Co.	Asset	✓			✓
Accts. Rec. — King Company	Asset	✓			✓
Admissions Revenue	Revenue		✓	✓	
Advertising Expense	Expense	✓		✓	
Cash in Bank	Asset	✓			✓
Clem Winter, Capital	Owner's Equity		✓		✓
Clem Winter, Withdrawals	Owner's Equity	✓		✓	✓
Concession Revenue	Revenue		✓	✓	
Miscellaneous Expense	Expense	✓		✓	
Office Furniture	Asset	✓			✓
Projection Equipment	Asset	✓			✓
Rent Expense	Expense	✓		✓	

Exercise 8-2, Page 163

	Beginning Capital	Investments	Revenue	Expenses	Withdrawals	Ending Capital
1.	$40,000	$ 500	$ 5,800	$3,400	$ 600	$42,300
2.	$24,075	$ 0	$14,980	$6,240	$ 900	$31,915
3.	$19,800	$ 1,000	$ 6,450	$6,980	$ 0	$20,270
4.	$ 0	$26,410	$ 5,920	$4,790	$ 200	$27,340
5.	$ 6,415	$ 0	$ 4,420	$3,975	$ 800	$6,060
6.	$20,870	$ 1,200	$12,980	$9,240	$1,200	$24,610

Problem 8-1, Page 163

Matura's Delivery Service
Income Statement
For the Month Ended April 30, 2003

Revenue:		
Delivery Fees		9309.00
Expenses:		
Advertising Expense	1852.00	
Delivery Expense	931.00	
Miscellaneous Expense	246.00	
Rent Expense	2400.00	
Utility Expense	604.00	
Total Expense		6033.00
Net Income		3276.00

Problem 8-2, Page 163

Matura's Delivery Service
Statement of Changes in Owner's Equity
For the Month Ended April 30, 2003

Beginning Capital, April 30, 2003		19089.00
Add: Investment	500.00	
Net Income	3276.00	
Total Increase in Capital		3776.00
Subtotal		22865.00
Less: Withdrawals		1500.00
Ending Capital, April 30, 2003		21365.00

Problem 8-5, Page 164
(1)

			BALANCE SHEET			INCOME STATEMENT			TRIAL BALANCE	
	ACCOUNT NAME	ACCT. NO.	CREDIT	DEBIT		CREDIT	DEBIT		CREDIT	DEBIT

Problem 8-5, Page 164 (Continued)
(2)

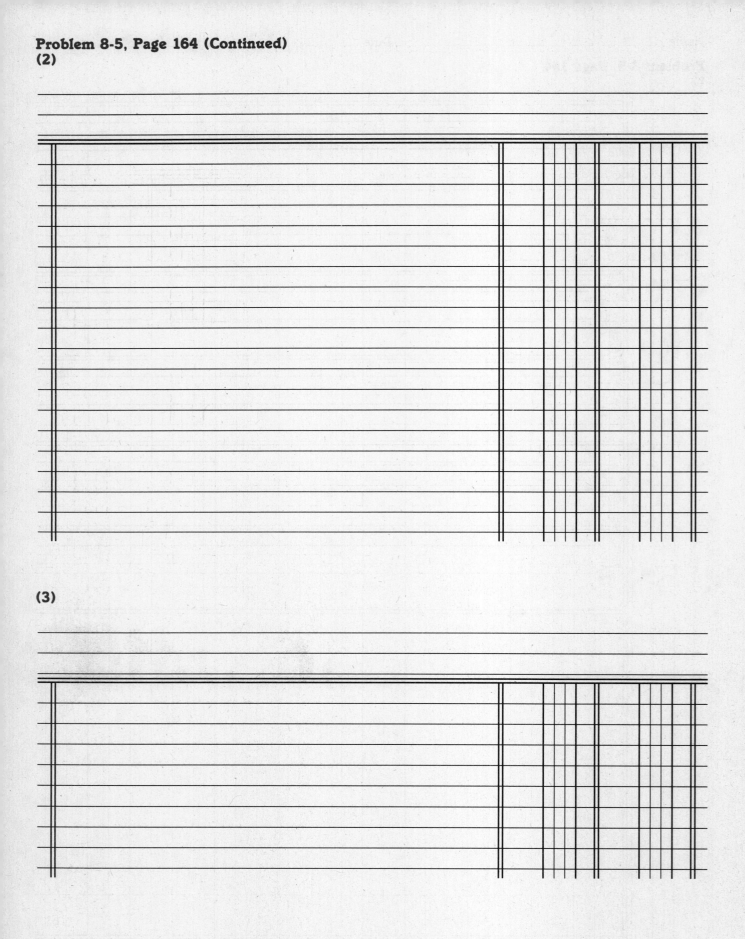

(3)

Problem 8-5, Page 164 (Concluded)
(4)

Problem 8-6, Page 165

Problem 8-7, Page 166

Total expenses: _____

Use this space for calculations.

Problem 9-5, Page 184
(1)

ACCT. NO.	ACCOUNT NAME	TRIAL BALANCE		INCOME STATEMENT		BALANCE SHEET	
		DEBIT	CREDIT	DEBIT	CREDIT	DEBIT	CREDIT
1							
2							
3							
4							
5							
6							
7							
8							
9							
10							
11							
12							
13							
14							
15							
16							
17							
18							
19							
20							
21							
22							
23							
24							
25							
26							

Problem 9-5, Page 184 (Continued)
(2)

Problem 9-5, Page 184 (Continued)
(2)

(3)

GENERAL JOURNAL   PAGE _____

	DATE		DESCRIPTION	POST. REF.	DEBIT	CREDIT	
1							1
2							2
3							3
4							4
5							5
6							6
7							7
8							8
9							9
10							10
11							11
12							12
13							13

GENERAL LEDGER (PARTIAL)

ACCOUNT *Alan Tsung, Capital*   ACCOUNT NO. 301

DATE		EXPLANATION	POST. REF.	DEBIT	CREDIT	BALANCE DEBIT	BALANCE CREDIT
19-- Apr.	1	Balance	✓				44675 00
	15		G11		10000 00		54675 00

ACCOUNT *Alan Tsung, Withdrawals*   ACCOUNT NO. 302

DATE		EXPLANATION	POST. REF.	DEBIT	CREDIT	BALANCE DEBIT	BALANCE CREDIT
19-- Apr.	30	Balance	✓			4000 00	

ACCOUNT *Income Summary*   ACCOUNT NO. 303

DATE	EXPLANATION	POST. REF.	DEBIT	CREDIT	BALANCE DEBIT	BALANCE CREDIT

ACCOUNT *Management Fees*   ACCOUNT NO. 401

DATE		EXPLANATION	POST. REF.	DEBIT	CREDIT	BALANCE DEBIT	BALANCE CREDIT
19-- Apr.	30	Balance	✓				9600 00

ACCOUNT *Advertising Expense*   ACCOUNT NO. 510

DATE		EXPLANATION	POST. REF.	DEBIT	CREDIT	BALANCE DEBIT	BALANCE CREDIT
19-- Apr.	30	Balance	✓			1000 00	

Problem 9-5, Page 184 (Concluded)
(4)

GENERAL LEDGER (PARTIAL)

ACCOUNT *Miscellaneous Expense*   ACCOUNT NO. _520_

DATE		EXPLANATION	POST. REF.	DEBIT	CREDIT	BALANCE DEBIT	BALANCE CREDIT
19-- Apr.	19	Balance	✓			400 00	

ACCOUNT *Rent Expense*   ACCOUNT NO. _530_

DATE		EXPLANATION	POST. REF.	DEBIT	CREDIT	BALANCE DEBIT	BALANCE CREDIT
19-- Apr.	1		G9			1200 00	

ACCOUNT *Utilities Expense*   ACCOUNT NO. _540_

DATE		EXPLANATION	POST. REF.	DEBIT	CREDIT	BALANCE DEBIT	BALANCE CREDIT
19-- Apr.	30	Balance	✓			375 00	

(5)

Problem 9-6, Page 185

GENERAL JOURNAL   PAGE __14__

	DATE		DESCRIPTION	POST. REF.	DEBIT	CREDIT	
1			*Closing Entries*				1
2	Nov. 19--	30	*Fees*		5 000 00		2
3			*Income Summary*			5 000 00	3
4		30	*Income Summary*		3 200 00		4
5			*Advertising Expense*			900 00	5
6			*Miscellaneous Expense*			300 00	6
7			*Rent Expense*			1 400 00	7
8			*Utilities Expense*			600 00	8
9		30	*Income Summary*		30 000 00		9
10			*Dale Bennett, Capital*			30 000 00	10
11		30	*Dale Bennett, Capital*		2 000 00		11
12			*Dale Bennett, Withdrawals*			2 000 00	12
13							13
14							14
15							15

(1) _____

_____

(2) _____

_____

(3) _____

_____

(4) _____

_____

(5) _____

_____

Name_____ Date_____ Class_____

Problem 11-3, Page 234 (Concluded)

GENERAL LEDGER (PARTIAL)

ACCOUNT *Accounts Receivable*   ACCOUNT NO. 102

DATE		EXPLANATION	POST. REF.	DEBIT	CREDIT	BALANCE DEBIT	BALANCE CREDIT
Sept.	1	Balance	✓			2697 50	

ACCOUNT *Sales Tax Payable*   ACCOUNT NO. 202

DATE		EXPLANATION	POST. REF.	DEBIT	CREDIT	BALANCE DEBIT	BALANCE CREDIT
Sept.	1	Balance	✓				316 45

ACCOUNT *Sales*   ACCOUNT NO. 401

DATE		EXPLANATION	POST. REF.	DEBIT	CREDIT	BALANCE DEBIT	BALANCE CREDIT
Sept.	1	Balance	✓				37962 50

Extra Form

ACCOUNT _____   ACCOUNT NO. _____

DATE	EXPLANATION	POST. REF.	DEBIT	CREDIT	BALANCE DEBIT	BALANCE CREDIT

Problem 11-4, Page 234

SALES JOURNAL

PAGE 20

	DATE	SALES SLIP NO.	CUSTOMER'S ACCOUNT DEBITED	POST. REF.	SALES CREDIT	SALES TAX PAYABLE CREDIT	ACCOUNTS RECEIVABLE DEBIT	
	19--							
26	Feb. 1	111	Chamber of Commerce	✓	40 00	1 20	41 20	26
27	3	112	Pantaleone's Funeral Home	✓	75 00	2 25	77 25	27
28	5	113	Tom Kristan	✓	20 00	60	20 60	28
29	7	114	First National Bank	✓	110 00	3 30	113 30	29
30	8	115	Marcy McCarver	✓	25 00	75	25 75	30
31	10	116	Linda Burton	✓	26 50	80	27 30	31
32	12	117	Jeff Daniels	✓	18 00	54	18 54	32
33	13	118	Pantaleone's Funeral Home	✓	90 00	2 70	92 70	33
34								34
35								35
36								36
37								37
38								38

SALES JOURNAL

PAGE _____

	DATE	SALES SLIP NO.	CUSTOMER'S ACCOUNT DEBITED	POST. REF.	SALES CREDIT	SALES TAX PAYABLE CREDIT	ACCOUNTS RECEIVABLE DEBIT	
1								1
2								2
3								3
4								4
5								5
6								6
7								7
8								8
9								9
10								10
11								11
12								12
13								13
14								14
15								15
16								16
17								17
18								18

Exercise 12-1, Page 258

```
┌────────────────────────────────────────────────────────┐
│                                                        │
│                                    RECEIPT             │
│  THE RUG CENTER                                        │
│                                    No. 203             │
│                                    _____ 19 ___   │
│                                                        │
│  Received From _____  │
│  _____ Dollars        │
│  For _____│
│                                                        │
│              Received By _____ │
│                                                        │
└────────────────────────────────────────────────────────┘
```

Exercise 12-2, Page 258

Sale Amount	Credit Terms	Cash Discount Amount	Amount of Cash Received
$4,600.00	2/10, n/30	$ 92.00	$4,508.00
1,500.00	n/30	0	$1500.00
2,760.00	1/10, n/30	$27.60	$2732.40
3,800.00	3/15, n/30	$114.00	$3686.00
450.30	n/30	0	$450.30
777.40	2/15, n/30	$15.55	$761.85
1,362.75	2/10, n/30	$27.26	$1335.49

Exercise 12-3, Page 258

Trans.	General Credit	Sales Credit	Sales Tax Payable Credit	Accounts Receivable Credit	Sales Discounts Debit	Cash in Bank Debit
1	✓					✓
2		✓	✓			✓
3				✓		✓
4		✓	✓			✓
5				✓	✓	✓
6	✓					✓

CASH RECEIPTS JOURNAL

PAGE ____

DATE	DOC. NO.	ACCOUNT TITLE	POST. REF.	GENERAL CREDIT	SALES CREDIT	SALES TAX PAYABLE CREDIT	ACCOUNTS RECEIVABLE CREDIT	SALES DISCOUNTS DEBIT	CASH IN BANK DEBIT

Problem 12-2, Page 259

ACCOUNTS RECEIVABLE SUBSIDIARY LEDGER

Name _Johanna Ambrose_

Address _3204 Dogwood Court, Louisville, KY 40201_

DATE	EXPLANATION	POST. REF.	DEBIT	CREDIT	BALANCE
19-- Nov. 1	Balance	✓			425 00

Name _David Dinsmore_

Address _635 Rolling Rock Road, Frankfort, KY 40601_

DATE	EXPLANATION	POST. REF.	DEBIT	CREDIT	BALANCE
19-- Nov. 1	Balance	✓			370 00

Name _Farrah Fletcher_

Address _835 Mt. Laurel Drive, Lexington, KY 40507_

DATE	EXPLANATION	POST. REF.	DEBIT	CREDIT	BALANCE
19-- Nov. 1	Balance	✓			250 00

Name _Richard Perry_

Address _479 Mountain Ash Road, Louisville, KY 40201_

DATE	EXPLANATION	POST. REF.	DEBIT	CREDIT	BALANCE
19-- Nov. 1	Balance	✓			340 00

ACCOUNTS RECEIVABLE SUBSIDIARY LEDGER

Name _Rachel Quinn_

Address _2456 Aspen Drive, Lexington, KY 40507_

DATE		EXPLANATION	POST. REF.	DEBIT	CREDIT	BALANCE
19-- Nov.	1	Balance	✓			275 00

Name _Stephen Walsh_

Address _1342 Willow Crossing, Frankfort, KY 40601_

DATE		EXPLANATION	POST. REF.	DEBIT	CREDIT	BALANCE
19-- Nov.	1	Balance	✓			362 00

GENERAL LEDGER (PARTIAL)

ACCOUNT _Cash in Bank_   ACCOUNT NO. _101_

DATE		EXPLANATION	POST. REF.	DEBIT	CREDIT	BALANCE DEBIT	BALANCE CREDIT
19-- Nov.	1	Balance	✓			9850 00	

ACCOUNT _Accounts Receivable_   ACCOUNT NO. _105_

DATE		EXPLANATION	POST. REF.	DEBIT	CREDIT	BALANCE DEBIT	BALANCE CREDIT
19-- Nov.	1	Balance	✓			2022 00	

ACCOUNT _Office Supplies_   ACCOUNT NO. _120_

DATE		EXPLANATION	POST. REF.	DEBIT	CREDIT	BALANCE DEBIT	BALANCE CREDIT
19-- Nov.	1	Balance	✓			690 00	

Problem 13-3, Page 285

PAGE 8

PURCHASES JOURNAL

DATE	INVOICE NO.	CREDITOR'S ACCOUNT CREDITED	POST. REF.	ACCOUNTS PAYABLE CREDIT	PURCHASES DEBIT	GENERAL ACCOUNT DEBITED	POST. REF.	DEBIT
19-- Nov. 4		Brought Forward	✓	726 00	726 00			

ACCOUNTS PAYABLE SUBSIDIARY LEDGER

Name _All South Circulation Co._

Address _1100 Peachtree Street NE, Atlanta, GA 30309_

DATE	EXPLANATION	POST. REF.	DEBIT	CREDIT	BALANCE
19-- Nov. 1	Balance	✓			361 40

Name _Central Supply_

Address _1600 North Jackson Avenue, San Jose, CA 95116_

DATE	EXPLANATION	POST. REF.	DEBIT	CREDIT	BALANCE

Name _Lake Equipment_

Address _3100 Yerba Buena Road, San Jose, CA 95135_

DATE	EXPLANATION	POST. REF.	DEBIT	CREDIT	BALANCE
19-- Nov. 1	Balance	✓			1219 00

Name _Longview Publications_

Address _200 South Orange Avenue, Orlando, FL 33101_

DATE	EXPLANATION	POST. REF.	DEBIT	CREDIT	BALANCE
19-- Nov. 1		P7		616 90	616 90

Name _Redstone Publishers_

Address _1500 South Michigan Avenue, Chicago, IL 60605_

DATE	EXPLANATION	POST. REF.	DEBIT	CREDIT	BALANCE
19-- Nov. 1	Balance	✓			157 20

Exercise 14-1, Page 310

Trans.	General Debit	Accounts Payable Debit	Purchases Discounts Credit	Cash in Bank Credit
1	✓			✓
2		✓	✓	✓
3	✓			✓
4	✓			✓
5	✓	✓		✓
6	✓			✓
7	✓			✓

Exercise 14-2, Page 310
(1)

The Corner Book Store
Schedule of Accounts Payable
December 31, 19--

Baker Publications	1 86 35	
Carswell Magazines	1 1 57 20	
Ridgwood, Inc.	2 63 0 25	
Petrocelli Publishing	5 61 1 90	
Junkins Supplies	41 9 38	
Beardsley Equipment	3 86 8 00	
Total Accounts Payable		13 87 3 08

(2)

The accounts payable has been proved since the
Accounts Payable account has a balance of $13873.08

Exercise 14-3, Page 310

Beginning Cash in Bank balance	7296.63
Plus: Cash receipts for the month	20956.47
Subtotal	28253.10
Less: Cash payments for the month	19975.12
Ending Cash in Bank balance	8277.98
Check stub balance	8277.98

PAGE _____

CASH PAYMENTS JOURNAL

DATE	DOC. NO.	ACCOUNT TITLE	POST. REF.	GENERAL DEBIT	ACCOUNTS PAYABLE DEBIT	PURCHASES DISCOUNTS CREDIT	CASH IN BANK CREDIT
1							
2							
3							
4							
5							
6							
7							
8							
9							
10							
11							
12							
13							
14							
15							
16							
17							
18							
19							
20							
21							
22							
23							
24							
25							
26							
27							
28							

Problem 14-2, Page 311

ACCOUNTS PAYABLE SUBSIDIARY LEDGER

Name _AAA Envelope Co._

Address _1400 Gulf Shore Drive, Fort Myers, FL 33904_

DATE	EXPLANATION	POST. REF.	DEBIT	CREDIT	BALANCE
19-- July 1	Balance	✓			1883 67

Name _Crawford Paper Products_

Address _105 Orange Avenue North, Orlando, FL 32801_

DATE	EXPLANATION	POST. REF.	DEBIT	CREDIT	BALANCE
19-- July 1	Balance	✓			9380 00

Name _Moore Paper Co._

Address _350 Biscayne Boulevard, Miami, FL 33132_

DATE	EXPLANATION	POST. REF.	DEBIT	CREDIT	BALANCE
19-- July 1	Balance	✓			1503 60

Name _Sam's, Inc._

Address _300 Davis Boulevard, Tampa, FL 33606_

DATE	EXPLANATION	POST. REF.	DEBIT	CREDIT	BALANCE
19-- July 1	Balance	✓			760 00

Problem 14-2, Page 311 (Continued)

GENERAL LEDGER (PARTIAL)

ACCOUNT _Cash in Bank_   ACCOUNT NO. _101_

DATE		EXPLANATION	POST. REF.	DEBIT	CREDIT	BALANCE DEBIT	BALANCE CREDIT
19-- July	1	Balance	✓			2163749	

ACCOUNT _Office Supplies_   ACCOUNT NO. _115_

DATE		EXPLANATION	POST. REF.	DEBIT	CREDIT	BALANCE DEBIT	BALANCE CREDIT
19-- July	1	Balance	✓			41625	

ACCOUNT _Office Furniture_   ACCOUNT NO. _130_

DATE		EXPLANATION	POST. REF.	DEBIT	CREDIT	BALANCE DEBIT	BALANCE CREDIT
19-- July	1	Balance	✓			469150	

ACCOUNT _Accounts Payable_   ACCOUNT NO. _210_

DATE		EXPLANATION	POST. REF.	DEBIT	CREDIT	BALANCE DEBIT	BALANCE CREDIT
19-- July	1	Balance	✓				1352727

ACCOUNT _Purchases_   ACCOUNT NO. _501_

DATE	EXPLANATION	POST. REF.	DEBIT	CREDIT	BALANCE DEBIT	BALANCE CREDIT

ACCOUNT _Transportation In_   ACCOUNT NO. _505_

DATE	EXPLANATION	POST. REF.	DEBIT	CREDIT	BALANCE DEBIT	BALANCE CREDIT

Problem 15-4, Page 335

Sept. 8 _____

_____

_____

_____

Sept. 12 _____

_____

_____

_____

Sept. 14 _____

_____

_____

_____

Sept. 20 _____

_____

_____

_____

Sept. 26 _____

_____

_____

_____

Problem 15-5, Page 335

GENERAL JOURNAL

PAGE _____

	DATE	DESCRIPTION	POST. REF.	DEBIT	CREDIT	
1						1
2						2
3						3
4						4
5						5
6						6
7						7
8						8
9						9
10						10
11						11
12						12
13						13
14						14
15						15
16						16
17						17
18						18
19						19
20						20
21						21
22						22
23						23
24						24
25						25
26						26
27						27
28						28
29						29
30						30
31						31
32						32
33						33
34						34
35						35
36						36
37						37
38						38

ADJUSTED TRIAL BALANCE		INCOME STATEMENT		BALANCE SHEET		
DEBIT	CREDIT	DEBIT	CREDIT	DEBIT	CREDIT	
						1
						2
						3
						4
						5
						6
						7
						8
						9
						10
						11
						12
						13
						14
						15
						16
						17
						18
						19
						20
						21
						22
						23
						24
						25
						26
						27
						28
						29
						30
						31
						32
						33
						34
						35
						36
						37
						38

Problem 18-5, Page 406 (Continued)

(4)

(5)

Problem 18-5, Page 406 (Continued)
(6), (7)

GENERAL JOURNAL

	DATE		DESCRIPTION	POST. REF.	DEBIT	CREDIT	
1							1
2							2
3							3
4							4
5							5
6							6
7							7
8							8
9							9
10							10
11							11
12							12
13							13
14							14
15							15
16							16
17							17
18							18
19							19
20							20
21							21
22							22
23							23
24							24
25							25
26							26
27							27
28							28
29							29
30							30
31							31
32							32
33							33
34							34
35							35
36							36
37							37
38							38

Name ______ Date ______ Class ______

Problem 18-5, Page 406 (Continued)
(8)

GENERAL LEDGER

ACCOUNT *Cash in Bank* ACCOUNT NO. 101

DATE		EXPLANATION	POST. REF.	DEBIT	CREDIT	BALANCE DEBIT	BALANCE CREDIT
19-- Dec.	1	Balance	✓			20,482 97	
	31		CR19	17,151 70		37,634 67	
	31		CP22		15,398 10	22,236 57	

ACCOUNT *Accounts Receivable* ACCOUNT NO. 105

DATE		EXPLANATION	POST. REF.	DEBIT	CREDIT	BALANCE DEBIT	BALANCE CREDIT
19-- Dec.	1	Balance	✓			11,194 38	
	7		G12		175 00	11,019 38	
	31		S17	6,951 62		17,971 00	
	31		CR19		10,571 00	7,400 00	

GENERAL LEDGER

ACCOUNT *Merchandise Inventory*   ACCOUNT NO. 110

DATE		EXPLANATION	POST. REF.	DEBIT	CREDIT	BALANCE	
						DEBIT	CREDIT
19-- Dec.	1	Balance	✓			25000 00	

ACCOUNT *Supplies*   ACCOUNT NO. 115

DATE		EXPLANATION	POST. REF.	DEBIT	CREDIT	BALANCE	
						DEBIT	CREDIT
19-- Dec.	1	Balance	✓			3966 50	
	10		P16	106 00		4072 50	
	21		P16	27 50		4100 00	

ACCOUNT *Prepaid Insurance*   ACCOUNT NO. 120

DATE		EXPLANATION	POST. REF.	DEBIT	CREDIT	BALANCE	
						DEBIT	CREDIT
19-- Dec.	1	Balance	✓			3000 00	

ACCOUNT *Equipment*   ACCOUNT NO. 150

DATE		EXPLANATION	POST. REF.	DEBIT	CREDIT	BALANCE	
						DEBIT	CREDIT
19-- Dec.	1	Balance	✓			67900 00	

ACCOUNT *Accounts Payable*   ACCOUNT NO. 201

DATE		EXPLANATION	POST. REF.	DEBIT	CREDIT	BALANCE	
						DEBIT	CREDIT
19-- Dec.	1	Balance	✓				13030 50
	19		G12	256 00			12774 50
	31		P16		9433 50		22208 00
	31		CP22	9208 00			13000 00

Problem 18-5, Page 406 (Continued)

GENERAL LEDGER

ACCOUNT *Federal Income Tax Payable*   ACCOUNT NO. 205

DATE	EXPLANATION	POST. REF.	DEBIT	CREDIT	BALANCE DEBIT	BALANCE CREDIT

ACCOUNT *Sales Tax Payable*   ACCOUNT NO. 210

DATE	EXPLANATION	POST. REF.	DEBIT	CREDIT	BALANCE DEBIT	BALANCE CREDIT
Dec. 1	Balance	✓				463 00
14		CP22	463 00			
31		S17		267 37		267 37
31		CR19		259 20		526 57

ACCOUNT *Capital Stock*   ACCOUNT NO. 301

DATE	EXPLANATION	POST. REF.	DEBIT	CREDIT	BALANCE DEBIT	BALANCE CREDIT
Dec. 1	Balance	✓				40 000 00

ACCOUNT *Retained Earnings*   ACCOUNT NO. 305

DATE	EXPLANATION	POST. REF.	DEBIT	CREDIT	BALANCE DEBIT	BALANCE CREDIT
Dec. 1	Balance	✓				25 400 00

ACCOUNT *Income Summary*   ACCOUNT NO. 310

DATE	EXPLANATION	POST. REF.	DEBIT	CREDIT	BALANCE DEBIT	BALANCE CREDIT

Problem 18-5, Page 406 (Continued)

GENERAL LEDGER

ACCOUNT *Sales* ACCOUNT NO. 401

DATE		EXPLANATION	POST. REF.	DEBIT	CREDIT	BALANCE DEBIT	BALANCE CREDIT
19-- Dec.	1	Balance	✓				161 835 75
	31		S17		6 684 25		168 520 00
	31		CR19		6 480 00		175 000 00

ACCOUNT *Sales Discounts* ACCOUNT NO. 405

DATE		EXPLANATION	POST. REF.	DEBIT	CREDIT	BALANCE DEBIT	BALANCE CREDIT
19-- Dec.	1	Balance	✓			3 616 50	
	31		CR19	158 50		3 775 00	

ACCOUNT *Sales Returns and Allowances* ACCOUNT NO. 410

DATE		EXPLANATION	POST. REF.	DEBIT	CREDIT	BALANCE DEBIT	BALANCE CREDIT
19-- Dec.	1	Balance	✓			2 325 00	
	7		G12	175 00		2 500 00	

ACCOUNT *Purchases* ACCOUNT NO. 501

DATE		EXPLANATION	POST. REF.	DEBIT	CREDIT	BALANCE DEBIT	BALANCE CREDIT
19-- Dec.	1	Balance	✓			64 385 00	
	11		CP22	1 615 00		66 000 00	
	31		P16	9 300 00		75 300 00	

ACCOUNT *Transportation In* ACCOUNT NO. 505

DATE		EXPLANATION	POST. REF.	DEBIT	CREDIT	BALANCE DEBIT	BALANCE CREDIT
19-- Dec.	1	Balance	✓			4 949 00	
	21		CP22	51 00		5 000 00	

Problem 18-5, Page 406 (Continued)

GENERAL LEDGER

ACCOUNT _Purchases Discounts_   ACCOUNT NO. _510_

DATE		EXPLANATION	POST. REF.	DEBIT	CREDIT	BALANCE	
						DEBIT	CREDIT
Dec. 19--	1	Balance	✓				2 162 00
	31		CP22		1 38 00		2 300 00

ACCOUNT _Purchases Returns and Allowances_   ACCOUNT NO. _515_

DATE		EXPLANATION	POST. REF.	DEBIT	CREDIT	BALANCE	
						DEBIT	CREDIT
Dec. 19--	1	Balance	✓				5 344 00
	19		G12		2 56 00		5 600 00

ACCOUNT _Bank Card Fees Expense_   ACCOUNT NO. _601_

DATE		EXPLANATION	POST. REF.	DEBIT	CREDIT	BALANCE	
						DEBIT	CREDIT
Dec. 19--	1	Balance	✓			3 253 00	
	27		CP22	2 62 00		3 515 00	

ACCOUNT _Insurance Expense_   ACCOUNT NO. _605_

DATE		EXPLANATION	POST. REF.	DEBIT	CREDIT	BALANCE	
						DEBIT	CREDIT

ACCOUNT _Miscellaneous Expense_   ACCOUNT NO. _610_

DATE		EXPLANATION	POST. REF.	DEBIT	CREDIT	BALANCE	
						DEBIT	CREDIT
Dec. 19--	1	Balance	✓			5 520 00	
	6		CP22	4 25 00		5 945 00	
	27		CP22	1 5 00		5 960 00	

GENERAL LEDGER

ACCOUNT _Rent Expense_   ACCOUNT NO. _615_

DATE		EXPLANATION	POST. REF.	DEBIT	CREDIT	BALANCE	
						DEBIT	CREDIT
Dec. 19--	1	Balance	✓			8 250 00	
	1		CP22	750 00		9 000 00	

ACCOUNT _Salaries Expense_   ACCOUNT NO. _620_

DATE		EXPLANATION	POST. REF.	DEBIT	CREDIT	BALANCE	
						DEBIT	CREDIT
Dec. 19--	1	Balance	✓			20 350 00	
	12		CP22	1 850 00		22 200 00	

ACCOUNT _Supplies Expense_   ACCOUNT NO. _625_

DATE		EXPLANATION	POST. REF.	DEBIT	CREDIT	BALANCE	
						DEBIT	CREDIT

ACCOUNT _Utilities Expense_   ACCOUNT NO. _630_

DATE		EXPLANATION	POST. REF.	DEBIT	CREDIT	BALANCE	
						DEBIT	CREDIT
Dec. 19--	1	Balance	✓			1 837 90	
	9		CP22	57 50		1 895 40	
	23		CP22	104 60		2 000 00	

ACCOUNT _Federal Income Tax Expense_   ACCOUNT NO. _640_

DATE		EXPLANATION	POST. REF.	DEBIT	CREDIT	BALANCE	
						DEBIT	CREDIT
Dec. 19--	1	Balance	✓			2 205 00	
	15		CP22	735 00		2 940 00	

Name _____ Date _____ Class _____

Problem 18-6, Page 407

GENERAL JOURNAL   PAGE _____

	DATE	DESCRIPTION	POST. REF.	DEBIT	CREDIT	
1						1
2						2
3						3
4						4
5						5
6						6
7						7
8						8
9						9
10						10
11						11
12						12
13						13
14						14
15						15
16						16
17						17
18						18
19						19
20						20
21						21
22						22
23						23
24						24
25						25
26						26
27						27
28						28
29						29
30						30
31						31
32						32
33						33
34						34
35						35
36						36
37						37
38						38

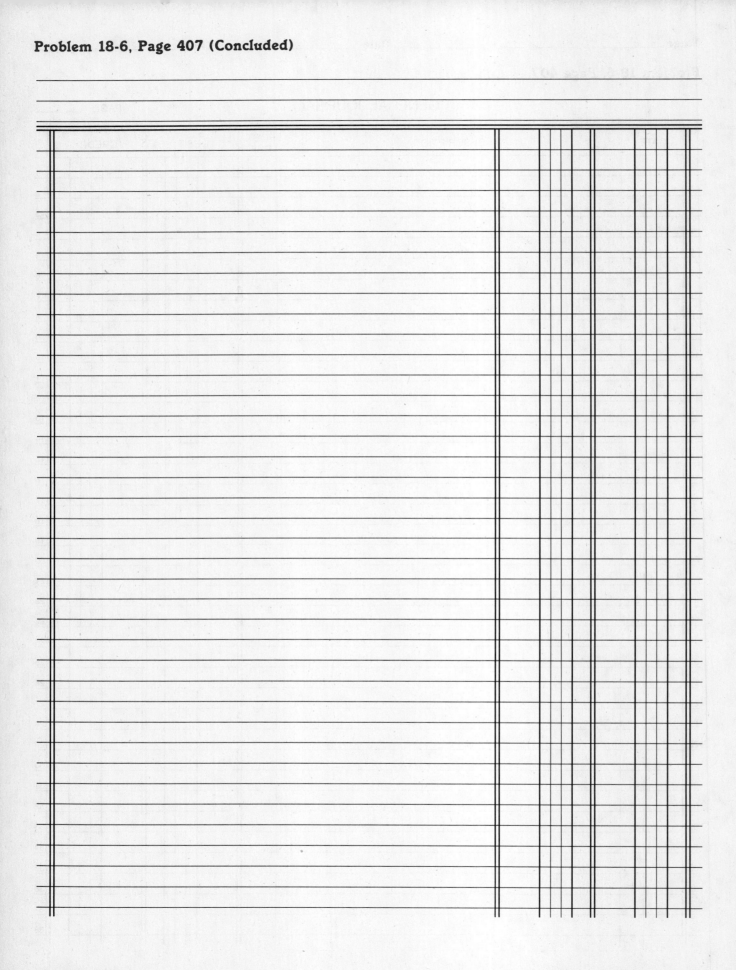

Application Activity 4, Pages 410-413

SALES JOURNAL

PAGE __22__

	DATE	SALES SLIP NO.	CUSTOMER'S ACCOUNT DEBITED	POST. REF.	SALES CREDIT	SALES TAX PAYABLE CREDIT	ACCOUNTS RECEIVABLE DEBIT	
1	19-- Dec. 7	479	Bulb-Tronics Suppliers	✓	1890 00	113 40	2003 40	1
2	9	480	Lumination Outlet	✓	1650 00	99 00	1749 00	2
3	9	481	Serendipity Shop	✓	1219 00	73 14	1292 14	3
4	12	482	Sparky Elec. Contractors	✓	875 00	52 50	927 50	4
5	15	483	The Kilowatt House	✓	1060 00	63 60	1123 60	5
6								6
7								7
8								8
9								9
10								10
11								11
12								12
13								13
14								14
15								15
16								16
17								17
18								18
19								19
20								20
21								21
22								22
23								23
24								24
25								25
26								26
27								27
28								28
29								29
30								30
31								31
32								32
33								33
34								34
35								35
36								36
37								37
38								38

CASH RECEIPTS JOURNAL

	DATE	DOC. NO.	ACCOUNT TITLE	POST. REF.	GENERAL CREDIT	SALES CREDIT	SALES TAX PAYABLE CREDIT	ACCOUNTS RECEIVABLE CREDIT	SALES DISCOUNTS DEBIT	CASH IN BANK DEBIT	
1	Dec. 2	R351	Bulb-Tronics Suppliers	✓				3195 90	60 30	3135 60	1
2	3	R352	Store Equipment	130	2000 00					2000 00	2
3	6	R353	Lumination Outlet	✓				1897 40	35 80	1861 60	3
4	8	R354	Serendipity Shop	✓				763 60	14 40	749 20	4
5	10	R355	Sparky Elec. Contractors	✓				1284 80		1284 80	5
6	12	R356	The Kilowatt House	✓				1240 20	23 40	1216 80	6
7	13	R357	Supplies	115	30 00					30 00	7
8	15	T40	Cash Sales	—		3650 70	219 04			3869 74	8
9	15	T40	Bank Card Sales	—		1812 40	108 74			1921 14	9
10											10
11											11
12											12
13											13
14											14
15											15
16											16
17											17
18											18
19											19
20											20
21											21
22											22
23											23
24											24
25											25
26											26
27											27
28											28

PURCHASES JOURNAL

PAGE 21

DATE	INVOICE NO.	CREDITOR'S ACCOUNT CREDITED	POST. REF.	ACCOUNTS PAYABLE CREDIT	PURCHASES DEBIT	GENERAL ACCOUNT DEBITED	POST. REF.	DEBIT
Dec. 3	CL213	Creative Lamps, Inc.	✓	150000	150000			
4	803	Taylor Office Suppliers	✓	12500		Office Equipment	125	12500
7	112	Brass Lamps, Ltd.	✓	260000	260000			
11	514	Stained Glass Outlet	✓	325000	325000			
14	326	Elec. Reflector Co.	✓	189000	189000			

CASH PAYMENTS JOURNAL

DATE	DOC. NO.	ACCOUNT TITLE	POST. REF.	GENERAL DEBIT	ACCOUNTS PAYABLE DEBIT	PURCHASES DISCOUNTS CREDIT	CASH IN BANK CREDIT	
19-- Dec. 2	601	Rent Expense	625	700 00			700 00	1
5	602	Brass Lamps, Ltd.	✓		1375 00	27 50	1347 50	2
6	603	Stained Glass Outlet	✓		1470 00	29 40	1440 60	3
7	604	Transportation In	505	37 20			37 20	4
9	605	Creative Lamps, Inc.	✓		1090 00	21 80	1068 20	5
11	606	Electrical Reflector Co.	✓		1235 00	24 70	1210 30	6
14	607	Reddi-Bright Manufacturing	✓		2280 00		2280 00	7
15	608	Utilities Expense	640	165 00			165 00	8
15	609	Taylor Office Suppliers	✓		125 00		125 00	9

GENERAL JOURNAL PAGE 12

	DATE		DESCRIPTION	POST. REF.	DEBIT	CREDIT	
1	19-- Dec.	3	Purchases	501	1 50 0 00		1
2			Merchandise Inventory	110		1 50 0 00	2
3			Memo 30				3
4		5	Sales Returns and Allowances	410	1 20 00		4
5			Sales Tax Payable	210	7 20		5
6			Accts. Rec./Sparky Elec. Contractors	105/✓		1 27 20	6
7			Credit Memo 43				7
8		12	Accts. Pay./Reddi-Bright Mfg.	201/✓	80 00		8
9			Purchases Returns + Allowances	515		80 00	9
10			Debit Memo 27				10
11							11
12							12
13							13
14							14
15							15
16							16
17							17
18							18
19							19
20							20
21							21
22							22
23							23
24							24
25							25
26							26
27							27
28							28
29							29
30							30
31							31
32							32
33							33
34							34
35							35
36							36
37							37
38							38

GENERAL JOURNAL

PAGE _____

	DATE	DESCRIPTION	POST. REF.	DEBIT	CREDIT	
1						1
2						2
3						3
4						4
5						5
6						6
7						7
8						8
9						9
10						10
11						11
12						12
13						13
14						14
15						15
16						16
17						17
18						18
19						19
20						20
21						21
22						22
23						23
24						24

ACCOUNTS RECEIVABLE SUBSIDIARY LEDGER

Name _Bulb-Tronics Suppliers_

Address _13400 Midway Road, Dallas, TX 75244_

DATE		EXPLANATION	POST. REF.	DEBIT	CREDIT	BALANCE
19-- Dec.	1	Balance	✓			3 1 9 5 90
	2		CR23		3 1 9 5 90	
	7		S22	2 0 0 3 40		2 0 0 3 40

Application Activity 4, Pages 410-413 (Continued)

ACCOUNTS RECEIVABLE SUBSIDIARY LEDGER

Name *Lumination Outlet*

Address *601 O'Hara Road, Arlington, TX 76010*

DATE		EXPLANATION	POST. REF.	DEBIT	CREDIT	BALANCE
19-- Dec.	1	Balance	✓			1 8 9 7 40
	6		CR23		1 8 9 7 40	
	9		S22	1 7 4 9 00		1 7 4 9 00

Name *Serendipity Shop*

Address *835 Coronado Drive, Corpus Christi, TX 78403*

DATE		EXPLANATION	POST. REF.	DEBIT	CREDIT	BALANCE
19-- Dec.	1	Balance	✓			7 63 60
	8		CR23		7 63 60	
	9		S22	1 2 9 2 14		1 2 9 2 14

Name *Sparky Electrical Contractors*

Address *103 Cedar Park, Dallas, TX 75244*

DATE		EXPLANATION	POST. REF.	DEBIT	CREDIT	BALANCE
19-- Dec.	1	Balance	✓			1 4 1 2 00
	5		G12		1 2 7 20	1 2 8 4 80
	10		CR23		1 2 8 4 80	
	12		S22	9 2 7 50		9 2 7 50

ACCOUNTS RECEIVABLE SUBSIDIARY LEDGER

Name _The Kilowatt House_

Address _70 South Washington Street, Fort Worth, TX 76101_

DATE		EXPLANATION	POST. REF.	DEBIT	CREDIT	BALANCE
19-- Dec.	1	Balance	✓			1240 20
	12		CR23		1240 20	—
	15		S22	1123 60		1123 60

ACCOUNTS PAYABLE SUBSIDIARY LEDGER

Name _Brass Lamps, Ltd._

Address _750 Peachtree Street NW, Atlanta, GA 30309_

DATE		EXPLANATION	POST. REF.	DEBIT	CREDIT	BALANCE
19-- Dec.	1	Balance	✓			1375 00
	5		CP24	1375 00		—
	7		P21		2600 00	2600 00

Name _Creative Lamps, Inc._

Address _1900 Talman Avenue North, Chicago, IL 60647_

DATE		EXPLANATION	POST. REF.	DEBIT	CREDIT	BALANCE
19-- Dec.	1	Balance	✓			1090 00
	3		P21		1500 00	2590 00
	9		CP24	1090 00		1500 00

Name _____ Date _____ Class _____

Application Activity 4, Pages 410-413 (Continued)

ACCOUNTS PAYABLE SUBSIDIARY LEDGER

Name _Electrical Reflector Co._

Address _989 Lenox Drive, Lexington, KY 40504_

DATE	EXPLANATION	POST. REF.	DEBIT	CREDIT	BALANCE
19-- Dec. 1	Balance	✓			1235 00
11		CP24	1235 00		
14		P21		1890 00	1890 00

Name _Reddi-Bright Manufacturing_

Address _700 Alamo Road, Abilene, TX 79605_

DATE	EXPLANATION	POST. REF.	DEBIT	CREDIT	BALANCE
19-- Dec. 1	Balance	✓			2360 00
12		G12	80 00		2280 00
14		CP24	2280 00		

Name _Stained Glass Outlet_

Address _150 Vista Avenue, St. Louis, MO 63110_

DATE	EXPLANATION	POST. REF.	DEBIT	CREDIT	BALANCE
19-- Dec. 1	Balance	✓			1470 00
6		CP24	1470 00		
11		P21		3250 00	3250 00

ACCOUNTS PAYABLE SUBSIDIARY LEDGER

Name **Taylor Office Suppliers**

Address **1500 Sandy Hill Road, Dallas, TX 75244**

DATE		EXPLANATION	POST. REF.	DEBIT	CREDIT	BALANCE
Dec.	4		P21		12500	12500
	15		CP24	12500		—

GENERAL LEDGER

ACCOUNT **Cash in Bank**   ACCOUNT NO. **101**

DATE		EXPLANATION	POST. REF.	DEBIT	CREDIT	BALANCE DEBIT	BALANCE CREDIT
Dec.	1	Balance	✓			1848029	

ACCOUNT **Accounts Receivable**   ACCOUNT NO. **105**

DATE		EXPLANATION	POST. REF.	DEBIT	CREDIT	BALANCE DEBIT	BALANCE CREDIT
Dec.	1	Balance	✓			850910	
	5		G12		12720	838190	

ACCOUNT **Merchandise Inventory**   ACCOUNT NO. **110**

DATE		EXPLANATION	POST. REF.	DEBIT	CREDIT	BALANCE DEBIT	BALANCE CREDIT
Dec.	1	Balance	✓			3176698	
	3		G12		150000	3026698	

Application Activity 4, Pages 410-413 (Continued)

GENERAL LEDGER

ACCOUNT _Supplies_   ACCOUNT NO. _115_

DATE		EXPLANATION	POST. REF.	DEBIT	CREDIT	BALANCE DEBIT	BALANCE CREDIT
Dec.	1	Balance	✓			1 25 1 46	
	13		CR23		30 00	1 22 1 46	

ACCOUNT _Prepaid Insurance_   ACCOUNT NO. _120_

DATE		EXPLANATION	POST. REF.	DEBIT	CREDIT	BALANCE DEBIT	BALANCE CREDIT
Dec.	1	Balance	✓			2 46 0 00	

ACCOUNT _Office Equipment_   ACCOUNT NO. _125_

DATE		EXPLANATION	POST. REF.	DEBIT	CREDIT	BALANCE DEBIT	BALANCE CREDIT
Dec.	1	Balance	✓			6 60 0 00	
	4		P21	1 25 00		6 72 5 00	

ACCOUNT _Store Equipment_   ACCOUNT NO. _130_

DATE		EXPLANATION	POST. REF.	DEBIT	CREDIT	BALANCE DEBIT	BALANCE CREDIT
Dec.	1	Balance	✓			10 80 0 00	
	3		CR23		20 0 00	10 60 0 00	

ACCOUNT _Accounts Payable_   ACCOUNT NO. _201_

DATE		EXPLANATION	POST. REF.	DEBIT	CREDIT	BALANCE DEBIT	BALANCE CREDIT
Dec.	1	Balance	✓				7 53 0 00
	12		G12	8 0 00			7 45 0 00

GENERAL LEDGER

ACCOUNT _Federal Income Tax Payable_   ACCOUNT NO. 205

DATE	EXPLANATION	POST. REF.	DEBIT	CREDIT	BALANCE DEBIT	BALANCE CREDIT

ACCOUNT _Sales Tax Payable_   ACCOUNT NO. 210

DATE		EXPLANATION	POST. REF.	DEBIT	CREDIT	BALANCE DEBIT	BALANCE CREDIT
Dec.¹⁹⁻⁻	1	Balance	✓				895 80
	5		G12	7 20			888 60

ACCOUNT _Capital Stock_   ACCOUNT NO. 301

DATE		EXPLANATION	POST. REF.	DEBIT	CREDIT	BALANCE DEBIT	BALANCE CREDIT
Dec.¹⁹⁻⁻	1	Balance	✓				25000 00

ACCOUNT _Retained Earnings_   ACCOUNT NO. 305

DATE		EXPLANATION	POST. REF.	DEBIT	CREDIT	BALANCE DEBIT	BALANCE CREDIT
Dec.¹⁹⁻⁻	1	Balance	✓				13000 00

ACCOUNT _Income Summary_   ACCOUNT NO. 310

DATE	EXPLANATION	POST. REF.	DEBIT	CREDIT	BALANCE DEBIT	BALANCE CREDIT

GENERAL LEDGER

ACCOUNT *Sales*   ACCOUNT NO. _401_

DATE		EXPLANATION	POST. REF.	DEBIT	CREDIT	BALANCE DEBIT	BALANCE CREDIT
19-- Dec.	1	Balance	✓				108 151 39

ACCOUNT *Sales Discounts*   ACCOUNT NO. _405_

DATE		EXPLANATION	POST. REF.	DEBIT	CREDIT	BALANCE DEBIT	BALANCE CREDIT
19-- Dec.	1	Balance	✓			2 10 00	

ACCOUNT *Sales Returns and Allowances*   ACCOUNT NO. _410_

DATE		EXPLANATION	POST. REF.	DEBIT	CREDIT	BALANCE DEBIT	BALANCE CREDIT
19-- Dec.	1	Balance	✓			1 75 40	
	5		G12	1 20 00		2 95 40	

ACCOUNT *Purchases*   ACCOUNT NO. _501_

DATE		EXPLANATION	POST. REF.	DEBIT	CREDIT	BALANCE DEBIT	BALANCE CREDIT
19-- Dec.	1	Balance	✓			23 761 13	
	3		G12	1 500 00		25 261 13	

GENERAL LEDGER

ACCOUNT _Transportation In_ ACCOUNT NO. 505

DATE		EXPLANATION	POST. REF.	DEBIT	CREDIT	BALANCE	
						DEBIT	CREDIT
19-- Dec.	1	Balance	✓			1275 80	
	7		CP24	37 20		1313 00	

ACCOUNT _Purchases Discounts_ ACCOUNT NO. 510

DATE		EXPLANATION	POST. REF.	DEBIT	CREDIT	BALANCE	
						DEBIT	CREDIT
19-- Dec.	1	Balance	✓				415 75

ACCOUNT _Purchases Returns and Allowances_ ACCOUNT NO. 515

DATE		EXPLANATION	POST. REF.	DEBIT	CREDIT	BALANCE	
						DEBIT	CREDIT
19-- Dec.	1	Balance	✓				390 85
	12		G12		80 00		470 85

ACCOUNT _Advertising Expense_ ACCOUNT NO. 605

DATE		EXPLANATION	POST. REF.	DEBIT	CREDIT	BALANCE	
						DEBIT	CREDIT
19-- Dec.	1	Balance	✓			430 00	

ACCOUNT _Bank Card Fees Expense_ ACCOUNT NO. 610

DATE		EXPLANATION	POST. REF.	DEBIT	CREDIT	BALANCE	
						DEBIT	CREDIT
19-- Dec.	1	Balance	✓			1420 57	

Application Activity 4, Pages 410-413 (Continued)

GENERAL LEDGER

ACCOUNT _Insurance Expense_ ACCOUNT NO. _615_

DATE	EXPLANATION	POST. REF.	DEBIT	CREDIT	BALANCE DEBIT	BALANCE CREDIT

ACCOUNT _Miscellaneous Expense_ ACCOUNT NO. _620_

DATE	EXPLANATION	POST. REF.	DEBIT	CREDIT	BALANCE DEBIT	BALANCE CREDIT
19-- Dec. 1	Balance	✓			247 52	

ACCOUNT _Rent Expense_ ACCOUNT NO. _625_

DATE	EXPLANATION	POST. REF.	DEBIT	CREDIT	BALANCE DEBIT	BALANCE CREDIT
19-- Dec. 1	Balance	✓			7 700 00	
2		CP24	700 00		8 400 00	

ACCOUNT _Salaries Expense_ ACCOUNT NO. _630_

DATE	EXPLANATION	POST. REF.	DEBIT	CREDIT	BALANCE DEBIT	BALANCE CREDIT
19-- Dec. 1	Balance	✓			34 871 18	

ACCOUNT _Supplies Expense_ ACCOUNT NO. _635_

DATE	EXPLANATION	POST. REF.	DEBIT	CREDIT	BALANCE DEBIT	BALANCE CREDIT

GENERAL LEDGER

ACCOUNT *Utilities Expense*   ACCOUNT NO. 640

DATE		EXPLANATION	POST. REF.	DEBIT	CREDIT	BALANCE	
						DEBIT	CREDIT
19-- Dec.	1	Balance	✓			2274 36	
	15		CP24	165 00		2439 36	

ACCOUNT *Federal Income Tax Expense*   ACCOUNT NO. 650

DATE		EXPLANATION	POST. REF.	DEBIT	CREDIT	BALANCE	
						DEBIT	CREDIT
19-- Dec.	1	Balance	✓			3150 00	

(6)

Application Activity 4, Pages 410-413 (Continued)
(7)

(7)

ACCT. NO.	ACCOUNT NAME	TRIAL BALANCE		ADJUSTMENTS	
		DEBIT	CREDIT	DEBIT	CREDIT
1					
2					
3					
4					
5					
6					
7					
8					
9					
10					
11					
12					
13					
14					
15					
16					
17					
18					
19					
20					
21					
22					
23					
24					
25					
26					
27					
28					
29					
30					
31					
32					
33					
34					
35					
36					
37					
38					

ADJUSTED TRIAL BALANCE		INCOME STATEMENT		BALANCE SHEET		
DEBIT	CREDIT	DEBIT	CREDIT	DEBIT	CREDIT	
						1
						2
						3
						4
						5
						6
						7
						8
						9
						10
						11
						12
						13
						14
						15
						16
						17
						18
						19
						20
						21
						22
						23
						24
						25
						26
						27
						28
						29
						30
						31
						32
						33
						34
						35
						36
						37
						38

Application Activity 4, Pages 410-413 (Continued)

(11)

(12)

Problem 19-4, Page 434

PAYROLL REGISTER

PAY PERIOD ENDING _____ 19 ___

DATE OF PAYMENT _____

EMPLOYEE NUMBER	NAME	MAR. STATUS	EXEMP.	TOTAL HOURS	RATE	EARNINGS			DEDUCTIONS							NET PAY	CK. NO.
						REGULAR	OVERTIME	TOTAL	SOC. SEC. TAX	MED. TAX	FED. INC. TAX	STATE INC. TAX	HOSP. INS.	OTHER	TOTAL		
1																	
2																	
3																	
4																	
5																	
6																	
7																	
8																	
9																	
10																	
11																	
12																	
13																	
14																	
15																	
16																	
17																	
18																	
19																	
20																	
21																	
22																	
23																	
24																	
25																	
	TOTALS																

Other Deductions: Write the appropriate code letter to the left of the amount: B—U.S. Savings Bonds; C—Credit Union; UD—Union Dues; UW—United Way.

PAYROLL REGISTER

PAY PERIOD ENDING _____ **19** ___ **DATE OF PAYMENT** _____

EMPLOYEE NUMBER	NAME	MAR. STATUS	EXEMP.	TOTAL HOURS	RATE	EARNINGS			DEDUCTIONS							NET PAY	CK. NO.
						REGULAR	OVERTIME	TOTAL	SOC. SEC. TAX	MED. TAX	FED. INC. TAX	STATE INC. TAX	HOSP. INS.	OTHER	TOTAL		
1																	
2																	
3																	
4																	
5																	
6																	
7																	
8																	
9																	
10																	
11																	
12																	
13																	
14																	
15																	
16																	
17																	
18																	
19																	
20																	
21																	
22																	
23																	
24																	
25																	
	TOTALS																

Other Deductions: Write the appropriate code letter to the left of the amount: B—U.S. Savings Bonds; C—Credit Union; UD—Union Dues; UW—United Way.

Problem 20-5, Page 457

CASH PAYMENTS JOURNAL   PAGE 16

	DATE	DOC. NO.	ACCOUNT TITLE	POST. REF.	GENERAL DEBIT	GENERAL CREDIT	ACCOUNTS PAYABLE DEBIT	PURCHASES DISCOUNTS CREDIT	CASH IN BANK CREDIT	
1	Sept. 15	—	Balance Brought Forward	✓	71194 6	7531 6	6462 00	71 08	12757 22	1
2	16	CK830	Advertising Expense	601	125 00				125 00	2
3										3
4										4
5										5
6										6
7										7
8										8
9										9
10										10
11										11
12										12
13										13
14										14
15										15
16										16
17										17
18										18
19										19
20										20
21										21
22										22
23										23
24										24
25										25

Problem 20-5, Page 457 (Concluded)

GENERAL JOURNAL

PAGE _____

	DATE		DESCRIPTION	POST. REF.	DEBIT	CREDIT	
1							1
2							2
3							3
4							4
5							5
6							6
7							7
8							8
9							9
10							10
11							11
12							12
13							13
14							14
15							15
16							16
17							17
18							18
19							19
20							20
21							21
22							22
23							23
24							24
25							25
26							26
27							27
28							28
29							29
30							30
31							31
32							32
33							33
34							34
35							35
36							36
37							37
38							38

Name _____ Date _____ Class _____

Application Activity 5, Pages 459-462

No.	019

Name __Carroll, Chris__

Soc. Sec. No. __049-71-8436__

Week Ending __7/29/--__

DAY	IN	OUT	IN	OUT	IN	OUT	TOTAL
M			2:00	5:00			
T			2:00	6:00			
W			3:00	5:00			
Th			2:00	6:00			
F			2:00	6:00			
S			9:00	2:00			
S							
						TOTAL HOURS	

	Hours	Rate	Amount
REGULAR			
OVERTIME			
TOTAL EARNINGS			

No.	018

Name __DeLuca, Ralph__

Soc. Sec. No. __223-56-0992__

Week Ending __7/29/--__

DAY	IN	OUT	IN	OUT	IN	OUT	TOTAL
M	9:00	12:00	12:30	5:00			
T	9:00	11:30	12:00	5:00			
W	9:00	1:00					
Th	9:00	12:00	12:30	4:00			
F	8:30	1:00	1:30	3:00			
S	9:00	1:30					
S							
						TOTAL HOURS	

	Hours	Rate	Amount
REGULAR			
OVERTIME			
TOTAL EARNINGS			

No.	013

Name __Gula, Gary__

Soc. Sec. No. __042-97-3814__

Week Ending __7/29/--__

DAY	IN	OUT	IN	OUT	IN	OUT	TOTAL
M	9:00	12:00	1:00	3:00			
T	9:00	12:00	1:00	5:00			
W	8:00	12:00	1:00	5:00			
Th	9:00	12:00	1:00	3:30			
F	9:00	12:00	1:00	4:00			
S	9:00	12:00					
S							
						TOTAL HOURS	

	Hours	Rate	Amount
REGULAR			
OVERTIME			
TOTAL EARNINGS			

No.	016

Name __Quinn, Betty__

Soc. Sec. No. __011-79-2118__

Week Ending __7/29/--__

DAY	IN	OUT	IN	OUT	IN	OUT	TOTAL
M	9:00	12:00	12:30	5:00			
T	9:00	12:30	1:00	6:00			
W	9:00	12:00	1:00	4:30			
Th	8:30	12:30	1:00	5:00			
F	9:00	11:30	12:00	5:00			
S	9:00	1:00					
S							
						TOTAL HOURS	

	Hours	Rate	Amount
REGULAR			
OVERTIME			
TOTAL EARNINGS			

SINGLE Persons—WEEKLY Payroll Period

If the wages are—		And the number of witholding allowances claimed is—										
At least	But less than	0	1	2	3	4	5	6	7	8	9	10
		The amount of income tax to be withheld is—										
$0	$50	$0	$0	$0	$0	$0	$0	$0	$0	$0	$0	$0
50	55	1	0	0	0	0	0	0	0	0	0	0
55	60	1	0	0	0	0	0	0	0	0	0	0
60	65	2	0	0	0	0	0	0	0	0	0	0
65	70	3	0	0	0	0	0	0	0	0	0	0
70	75	4	0	0	0	0	0	0	0	0	0	0
75	80	4	0	0	0	0	0	0	0	0	0	0
80	85	5	0	0	0	0	0	0	0	0	0	0
85	90	6	0	0	0	0	0	0	0	0	0	0
90	95	7	0	0	0	0	0	0	0	0	0	0
95	100	7	1	0	0	0	0	0	0	0	0	0
100	105	8	1	0	0	0	0	0	0	0	0	0
105	110	9	2	0	0	0	0	0	0	0	0	0
110	115	10	3	0	0	0	0	0	0	0	0	0
115	120	10	4	0	0	0	0	0	0	0	0	0
120	125	11	4	0	0	0	0	0	0	0	0	0
125	130	12	5	0	0	0	0	0	0	0	0	0
130	135	13	6	0	0	0	0	0	0	0	0	0
135	140	13	7	0	0	0	0	0	0	0	0	0
140	145	14	7	1	0	0	0	0	0	0	0	0
145	150	15	8	1	0	0	0	0	0	0	0	0
150	155	16	9	2	0	0	0	0	0	0	0	0
155	160	16	10	3	0	0	0	0	0	0	0	0
160	165	17	10	4	0	0	0	0	0	0	0	0
165	170	18	11	4	0	0	0	0	0	0	0	0
170	175	19	12	5	0	0	0	0	0	0	0	0
175	180	19	13	6	0	0	0	0	0	0	0	0
180	185	20	13	7	0	0	0	0	0	0	0	0
185	190	21	14	7	1	0	0	0	0	0	0	0
190	195	22	15	8	1	0	0	0	0	0	0	0
195	200	22	16	9	2	0	0	0	0	0	0	0
200	210	23	17	10	3	0	0	0	0	0	0	0
210	220	25	18	11	5	0	0	0	0	0	0	0
220	230	26	10	13	6	0	0	0	0	0	0	0
230	240	28	21	14	8	1	0	0	0	0	0	0

MARRIED Persons—WEEKLY Payroll Period

If the wages are—		And the number of witholding allowances claimed is—										
At least	But less than	0	1	2	3	4	5	6	7	8	9	10
		The amount of income tax to be withheld is—										
$195	$200	$12	$5	$0	$0	$0	$0	$0	$0	$0	$0	$0
200	210	13	6	0	0	0	0	0	0	0	0	0
210	220	14	8	1	0	0	0	0	0	0	0	0
220	230	16	9	2	0	0	0	0	0	0	0	0
230	240	17	11	4	0	0	0	0	0	0	0	0
240	250	19	12	5	0	0	0	0	0	0	0	0
250	260	20	14	7	0	0	0	0	0	0	0	0
260	270	22	15	8	2	0	0	0	0	0	0	0
270	280	23	17	10	3	0	0	0	0	0	0	0
280	290	25	18	11	5	0	0	0	0	0	0	0
290	300	26	20	13	6	0	0	0	0	0	0	0
300	310	28	21	14	8	1	0	0	0	0	0	0
310	320	29	23	16	9	2	0	0	0	0	0	0
320	330	31	24	17	11	4	0	0	0	0	0	0
330	340	32	26	19	12	5	0	0	0	0	0	0
340	350	34	27	20	14	7	0	0	0	0	0	0
350	360	35	29	22	15	8	1	0	0	0	0	0
360	370	37	30	23	17	10	3	0	0	0	0	0
370	380	38	32	25	18	11	4	0	0	0	0	0
380	390	40	33	26	20	13	6	0	0	0	0	0
390	400	41	35	28	21	14	7	1	0	0	0	0
400	410	43	36	29	23	16	9	2	0	0	0	0
410	420	44	38	31	24	17	10	4	0	0	0	0
420	430	46	39	32	26	19	12	5	0	0	0	0
430	440	47	41	34	27	20	13	7	0	0	0	0
440	450	49	42	35	29	22	15	8	1	0	0	0
450	460	50	44	37	30	23	16	10	3	0	0	0
460	470	52	45	38	32	25	18	11	4	0	0	0
470	480	53	47	40	33	26	19	13	6	0	0	0
480	490	55	48	41	35	28	21	14	7	1	0	0
490	500	56	50	43	36	29	22	16	9	2	0	0
500	510	58	51	44	38	31	24	17	10	4	0	0
510	520	59	53	46	39	32	25	19	12	5	0	0
520	530	61	54	47	41	34	27	20	13	7	0	0
530	540	62	56	49	42	35	28	22	15	8	1	0

Application Activity 5, Pages 459-462 (Continued)

MASSACHUSETTS DOR (Department of Revenue)

If the payroll period with respect to an employee is WEEKLY

And the wages are		And the number of withholding exemptions claimed is:										
At least	But less than	0	1	2	3	4	5	6	7	8	9	10
		The amount of Massachusetts income tax to be withheld shall be:										
$ 1 150	$150 160	5% $ 7.20	$ .00 5.08	$ .00 4.12	$ .00 3.16	$ .00 2.20	$ .00 1.23	$ .00 .27	$ .00 .00	$ .00 .00	$ .00 .00	$ .00 .00
160	170	7.66	5.54	4.58	3.62	2.66	1.70	.74	.00	.00	.00	.00
170	180	8.12	6.01	5.05	4.09	3.12	2.16	1.20	.24	.00	.00	.00
180	190	8.59	6.47	5.51	4.55	3.59	2.63	1.67	.70	.00	.00	.00
190	200	9.05	6.94	5.98	5.01	4.05	3.09	2.13	1.17	.21	.00	.00
200	210	9.52	7.40	6.44	5.48	4.52	3.56	2.59	1.63	.67	.00	.00
210	220	9.98	7.87	6.90	5.94	4.98	4.02	3.06	2.10	1.14	.17	.00
220	230	10.45	8.33	7.37	6.41	5.45	4.48	3.52	2.56	1.60	.64	.00
230	240	10.91	8.79	7.83	6.87	5.91	4.95	3.99	3.03	2.06	1.10	.14
240	250	11.37	9.26	8.30	7.34	6.37	5.41	4.45	3.49	2.53	1.57	.60
250	260	11.84	9.72	8.76	7.80	6.84	5.88	4.92	3.95	2.99	2.03	1.07
260	270	12.30	10.19	9.23	8.26	7.30	6.34	5.38	4.42	3.46	2.49	1.53
270	280	12.77	10.65	9.69	8.73	7.77	6.81	5.84	4.88	3.92	2.96	2.00
280	290	13.23	11.12	10.15	9.19	8.23	7.27	6.31	5.35	4.38	3.42	2.46
290	300	13.70	11.58	10.62	9.66	8.70	7.73	6.77	5.81	4.85	3.89	2.93
300	310	14.16	12.04	11.08	10.12	9.16	8.20	7.24	6.28	5.31	4.35	3.39
310	320	14.62	12.51	11.55	10.59	9.62	8.66	7.70	6.74	5.78	4.82	3.85
320	330	15.09	12.97	12.01	11.05	10.09	9.13	8.17	7.20	6.24	5.28	4.32
330	340	15.55	13.44	12.48	11.51	10.55	9.59	8.63	7.67	6.71	5.74	4.78
340	350	16.02	13.90	12.94	11.98	11.02	10.06	9.09	8.13	7.17	6.21	5.25
350	360	16.48	14.37	13.40	12.44	11.48	10.52	9.56	8.60	7.63	6.67	5.71
360	370	16.95	14.83	13.87	12.91	11.95	10.98	10.02	9.06	8.10	7.14	6.18
370	380	17.41	15.29	14.33	13.37	12.41	11.45	10.49	9.52	8.56	7.60	6.64
380	390	17.87	15.76	14.80	13.84	12.87	11.91	10.95	9.99	9.03	8.07	7.10
390	400	18.34	16.22	15.26	14.30	13.34	12.38	11.41	10.45	9.49	8.53	7.57
400	410	18.80	16.69	15.73	14.76	13.80	12.84	11.88	10.92	9.96	8.99	8.03
410	420	19.27	17.15	16.19	15.23	14.27	13.30	12.34	11.38	10.42	9.46	8.50
420	430	19.73	17.62	16.65	15.69	14.73	13.77	12.81	11.85	10.88	9.92	8.96
430	440	20.19	18.08	17.12	16.16	15.19	14.23	13.27	12.31	11.35	10.39	9.43
440	450	20.66	18.54	17.58	16.62	15.66	14.70	13.74	12.77	11.81	10.85	9.89
450	460	21.12	19.01	18.05	17.08	16.12	15.16	14.20	13.24	12.28	11.32	10.35
460	470	21.59	19.47	18.51	17.55	16.59	15.63	14.66	13.70	12.74	11.78	10.82
470	480	22.05	19.94	18.97	18.01	17.05	16.09	15.13	14.17	13.21	12.24	11.28
480	490	22.52	20.40	19.44	18.48	17.52	16.55	15.59	14.63	13.67	12.71	11.75
490	500	22.98	20.86	19.90	18.94	17.98	17.02	16.06	15.10	14.13	13.17	12.21
500	510	23.44	21.33	20.37	19.41	18.44	17.48	16.52	15.56	14.60	13.64	12.68
510	520	23.91	21.79	20.83	19.87	18.91	17.95	16.99	16.02	15.06	14.10	13.14
520	530	24.37	22.26	21.30	20.33	19.37	18.41	17.45	16.49	15.53	14.57	13.60
530	540	24.84	22.72	21.76	20.80	19.84	18.88	17.91	16.95	15.99	15.03	14.07
540	550	25.33	23.21	22.25	21.29	20.33	19.37	18.40	17.44	16.48	15.52	14.56
550	560	25.83	23.71	22.75	21.79	20.83	19.87	18.90	17.94	16.98	16.02	15.06
560	570	26.33	24.21	23.25	22.29	21.33	20.37	19.40	18.44	17.48	16.52	15.56
570	580	26.83	24.71	23.75	22.79	21.83	20.87	19.90	18.94	17.98	17.02	16.06
580	590	27.33	25.21	24.25	23.29	22.33	21.37	20.40	19.44	18.48	17.52	16.56
590	600	27.83	25.71	24.75	23.79	22.83	21.87	20.90	19.94	18.98	18.02	17.06
600	610	28.33	26.21	25.25	24.29	23.33	22.37	21.40	20.44	19.48	18.52	17.56
610	620	28.83	26.71	25.75	24.79	23.83	22.87	21.90	20.94	19.98	19.02	18.06
620	630	29.33	27.21	26.25	25.29	24.33	23.37	22.40	21.44	20.48	19.52	18.56
630	640	29.83	27.71	26.75	25.79	24.83	23.87	22.90	21.94	20.98	20.02	19.06
640	650	30.33	28.21	27.25	26.29	25.33	24.37	23.40	22.44	21.48	20.52	19.56
650	660	30.83	28.71	27.75	26.79	25.83	24.87	23.90	22.94	21.98	21.02	20.06

PAYROLL REGISTER

PAY PERIOD ENDING _____

DATE OF PAYMENT _____

19 ____

EMPLOYEE NUMBER	NAME	MAR. STATUS	EXEMP.	TOTAL HOURS	RATE	EARNINGS			DEDUCTIONS							NET PAY	CK. NO.
						REGULAR	OVERTIME	TOTAL	SOC. SEC. TAX	MED. TAX	FED. INC. TAX	STATE INC. TAX	HOSP. INS.	OTHER	TOTAL		
1																	1
2																	2
3																	3
4																	4
5																	5
6																	6
7																	7
8																	8
9																	9
10																	10
11																	11
12																	12
13																	13
14																	14
15																	15
16																	16
17																	17
18																	18
19																	19
20																	20
21																	21
22																	22
23																	23
24																	24
25																	25
	TOTALS																

Other Deductions: Write the appropriate code letter to the left of the amount: B—U.S. Savings Bonds; C—Credit Union; UD—Union Dues; UW—United Way.

Application Activity 5, Pages 459-462 (Continued)

$ _____ No. 972

DATE _____ 19 _____

TO _____

FOR _____

	DOLLARS	CENTS
BAL. BRO. FWD.	6,371	42
ADD DEPOSITS		
TOTAL		
LESS THIS CHECK		
BAL. CARR. FWD.		

THE GREENS
1500 Main Street
Concord, MA 01742

_____ 19 _____ 53-215 / 113

No. 972

PAY TO THE
ORDER OF _____ $ _____

_____ DOLLARS

PATRIOT BANK
Concord, Massachusetts

⑈011302153⑈ 331 234 9⑈ 0972

$ _____ No. 973

DATE _____ 19 _____

TO _____

FOR _____

	DOLLARS	CENTS
BAL. BRO. FWD.		
ADD DEPOSITS		
TOTAL		
LESS THIS CHECK		
BAL. CARR. FWD.		

THE GREENS
1500 Main Street
Concord, MA 01742

_____ 19 _____ 53-215 / 113

No. 973

PAY TO THE
ORDER OF _____ $ _____

_____ DOLLARS

PATRIOT BANK
Concord, Massachusetts

⑈011302153⑈ 331 234 9⑈ 0973

$ _____ No. 974

DATE _____ 19 _____

TO _____

FOR _____

	DOLLARS	CENTS
BAL. BRO. FWD.		
ADD DEPOSITS		
TOTAL		
LESS THIS CHECK		
BAL. CARR. FWD.		

THE GREENS
1500 Main Street
Concord, MA 01742

_____ 19 _____ 53-215 / 113

No. 974

PAY TO THE
ORDER OF _____ $ _____

_____ DOLLARS

PATRIOT BANK
Concord, Massachusetts

⑈011302153⑈ 331 234 9⑈ 0974

THE GREENS PAYROLL ACCOUNT
1500 Main Street
Concord, MA 01742

DATE _____ 19 _____

Checks and other items are received for deposit subject to
the terms and conditions of this bank's collection agreement.

PATRIOT BANK
Concord, Massachusetts

⑈011302153⑈ 0001 290 3⑈

		DOLLARS	CENTS
	Cash		
	1 CHECKS—LIST SINGLY		
	2		
	3		
	4		
	5		
	6		
	7		
	8		
	TOTAL		

BE SURE EACH ITEM IS ENDORSED

THE GREEENS PAYROLL ACCOUNT
1500 Main Street
Concord, MA 01742

No. 310

19_____ 53-215
113

Pay to the
Order of _____ $ _____

_____ Dollars

PATRIOT BANK
Concorde, Massachusetts

⑈011302153⑈ 0001 290 3⑈ 0310 _____

- -

Employee Pay Statement
Detach and retain this statement.

No. 310

Period Ending	Earnings			Deductions							Net Pay
	Regular	Overtime	Total	Soc. Sec. Tax	Med. Tax	Federal Income Tax	State Income Tax	Hosp. Ins.	Other	Total	

THE GREEENS PAYROLL ACCOUNT
1500 Main Street
Concord, MA 01742

No. 311

19_____ 53-215
113

Pay to the
Order of _____ $ _____

_____ Dollars

PATRIOT BANK
Concorde, Massachusetts

⑈011302153⑈ 0001 290 3⑈ 0311 _____

- -

Employee Pay Statement
Detach and retain this statement.

No. 311

Period Ending	Earnings			Deductions							Net Pay
	Regular	Overtime	Total	Soc. Sec. Tax	Med. Tax	Federal Income Tax	State Income Tax	Hosp. Ins.	Other	Total	

Application Activity 5, Pages 459-462 (Continued)

THE GREEENS PAYROLL ACCOUNT   No. 312
1500 Main Street
Concord, MA 01742   19 _____   53-215
                                                        ───────
                                                          113
Pay to the
Order of _____ $ _____

_____ Dollars

PATRIOT BANK
Concorde, Massachusetts

⑈011302153⑈ 0001 290 3⑈ 0312   _____

Employee Pay Statement   No. 312
Detach and retain this statement.

Period Ending	Earnings			Deductions							Net Pay
	Regular	Overtime	Total	Soc. Sec. Tax	Med. Tax	Federal Income Tax	State Income Tax	Hosp. Ins.	Other	Total	

THE GREEENS PAYROLL ACCOUNT   No. 313
1500 Main Street
Concord, MA 01742   19 _____   53-215
                                                        ───────
                                                          113
Pay to the
Order of _____ $ _____

_____ Dollars

PATRIOT BANK
Concorde, Massachusetts

⑈011302153⑈ 0001 290 3⑈ 0313   _____

Employee Pay Statement   No. 313
Detach and retain this statement.

Period Ending	Earnings			Deductions							Net Pay
	Regular	Overtime	Total	Soc. Sec. Tax	Med. Tax	Federal Income Tax	State Income Tax	Hosp. Ins.	Other	Total	

THE GREEENS PAYROLL ACCOUNT   No. 314

1500 Main Street
Concord, MA 01742

_____ 19_____ 53-215
                                            ─────
                                             113

Pay to the
Order of _____ $ _____

_____ Dollars

PATRIOT BANK
Concorde, Massachusetts

⑆011302153⑆ 0001 290 3⑈ 0314   _____

- -

Employee Pay Statement   No. 314
Detach and retain this statement.

Period Ending	Earnings			Deductions							Net Pay
	Regular	Overtime	Total	Soc. Sec. Tax	Med. Tax	Federal Income Tax	State Income Tax	Hosp. Ins.	Other	Total	

THE GREEENS PAYROLL ACCOUNT   No. 315

1500 Main Street
Concord, MA 01742

_____ 19_____ 53-215
                                            ─────
                                             113

Pay to the
Order of _____ $ _____

_____ Dollars

PATRIOT BANK
Concorde, Massachusetts

⑆011302153⑆ 0001 290 3⑈ 0315   _____

- -

Employee Pay Statement   No. 315
Detach and retain this statement.

Period Ending	Earnings			Deductions							Net Pay
	Regular	Overtime	Total	Soc. Sec. Tax	Med. Tax	Federal Income Tax	State Income Tax	Hosp. Ins.	Other	Total	

Application Activity 5, Pages 459-462 (Continued)

THE GREEENS PAYROLL ACCOUNT
1500 Main Street
Concord, MA 01742

No. 316

19_____ $\frac{53\text{-}215}{113}$

Pay to the
Order of _____ $ _____

_____ Dollars

PATRIOT BANK
Concorde, Massachusetts

⑆011302153⑆ 0001 290 3⑆ 0316 _____

- -

Employee Pay Statement
Detach and retain this statement.

No. 316

Period Ending	Earnings			Deductions							Net Pay
	Regular	Overtime	Total	Soc. Sec. Tax	Med. Tax	Federal Income Tax	State Income Tax	Hosp. Ins.	Other	Total	

THE GREEENS PAYROLL ACCOUNT
1500 Main Street
Concord, MA 01742

No. 317

19_____ $\frac{53\text{-}215}{113}$

Pay to the
Order of _____ $ _____

_____ Dollars

PATRIOT BANK
Concorde, Massachusetts

⑆011302153⑆ 0001 290 3⑆ 0317 _____

- -

Employee Pay Statement
Detach and retain this statement.

No. 317

Period Ending	Earnings			Deductions							Net Pay
	Regular	Overtime	Total	Soc. Sec. Tax	Med. Tax	Federal Income Tax	State Income Tax	Hosp. Ins.	Other	Total	

EMPLOYEE'S EARNINGS RECORD FOR QUARTER ENDING September 30, 19--

Carroll, Christopher E.
Last Name First Initial

EMPLOYEE NO. 019 MARITAL STATUS S EXEMPTIONS 1

31 Wachusetts Street
Address

POSITION Stock Clerk

Concord, MA 01742

RATE OF PAY $4.90/hr. SOC. SEC. NO. 049-71-8431

PAY PERIOD		EARNINGS			DEDUCTIONS							NET PAY	ACCUMULATED EARNINGS
NO.	ENDED	REGULAR	OVERTIME	TOTAL	SOC. SEC. TAX	MED. TAX	FED. INC. TAX	STATE INC. TAX	HOSP. INS.	OTHER	TOTAL		1,966 13
1	7/8	102 90		102 90	6 38	1 49	2 00	—	2 75	(B) 5 00	17 62	85 28	2,069 03
2	7/15	85 75		85 75	5 32	1 24	—	—	2 75	(B) 5 00	14 31	71 44	2,154 78
3	7/22	96 78		96 78	6 00	1 40	—	—	2 75	(B) 5 00	15 15	81 63	2,251 56
4													
5													
6													
7													
8													
9													
10													
11													
12													
13													
QUARTERLY TOTALS													

Other Deductions: B—U.S. Savings Bonds; C—Credit Union; UD—Union Dues; UW—United Way.

EMPLOYEE'S EARNINGS RECORD FOR QUARTER ENDING _September 30, 19--_

Last Name: Holland   First: Anne   Initial: K.
Address: 98 Pearl Street
Cambridge, MA 02139

MARITAL STATUS: M   EXEMPTIONS: 2
EMPLOYEE NO.: 011
POSITION: Salesperson
RATE OF PAY: $175.00 salary / 10% commission
SOC. SEC. NO.: 027-10-3248

| PAY PERIOD | | EARNINGS | | | DEDUCTIONS | | | | | | | NET PAY | ACCUMULATED EARNINGS |
NO.	ENDED	REGULAR	OVERTIME	TOTAL	SOC. SEC. TAX	MED. TAX	FED. INC. TAX	STATE INC. TAX	HOSP. INS.	OTHER	TOTAL		
													5,538 92
1	7/8	283 60		283 60	17 58	4 11	13 00	10 15	4 55	(B) 5 00	54 39	229 21	5,822 52
2	7/15	259 10		259 10	16 06	3 76	12 00	8 76	4 55	(B) 5 00	50 13	208 97	6,081 62
3	7/22	238 91		238 91	14 81	3 46	11 00	7 83	4 55	(B) 5 00	46 65	192 26	6,320 53
4													
5													
6													
7													
8													
9													
10													
11													
12													
13													
QUARTERLY TOTALS													

Other Deductions: B—U.S. Savings Bonds; C—Credit Union; UD—Union Dues; UW—United Way.

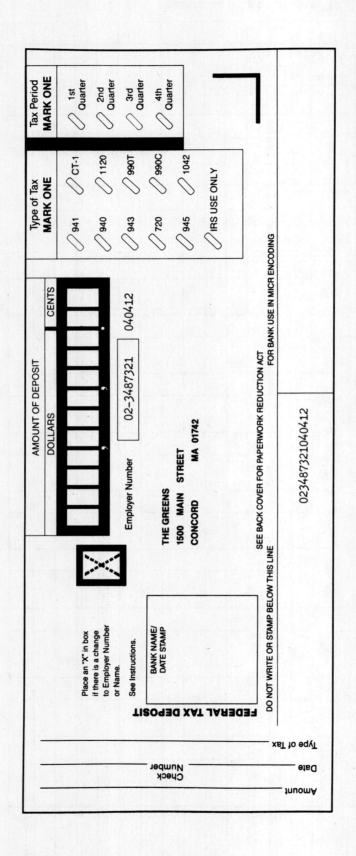

Application Activity 5, Pages 459-462 (Continued)

CASH PAYMENTS JOURNAL

PAGE 19

DATE	DOC. NO.	ACCOUNT TITLE	POST. REF.	GENERAL DEBIT	GENERAL CREDIT	ACCOUNTS PAYABLE DEBIT	PURCHASES DISCOUNTS CREDIT	CASH IN BANK CREDIT
19-- July 29	—	Balance Brought Forward	✓	1146542	60342	941600	11770	2016030

GENERAL JOURNAL

PAGE _____

	DATE	DESCRIPTION	POST. REF.	DEBIT	CREDIT	
1						1
2						2
3						3
4						4
5						5
6						6
7						7
8						8
9						9
10						10
11						11
12						12
13						13
14						14
15						15
16						16
17						17
18						18

GENERAL LEDGER (PARTIAL)

ACCOUNT *Employees' Federal Income Tax Payable*   ACCOUNT NO. 205

DATE	EXPLANATION	POST. REF.	DEBIT	CREDIT	BALANCE DEBIT	BALANCE CREDIT
19-- July 22	Balance	✓				183 00

ACCOUNT *Employees' State Income Tax Payable*   ACCOUNT NO. 210

DATE	EXPLANATION	POST. REF.	DEBIT	CREDIT	BALANCE DEBIT	BALANCE CREDIT
19-- July 22	Balance	✓				245 74

Application Activity 5, Pages 459-462 (Continued)

GENERAL LEDGER (PARTIAL)

ACCOUNT *Social Security Tax Payable*　　　　　　ACCOUNT NO. **215**

DATE	EXPLANATION	POST. REF.	DEBIT	CREDIT	BALANCE DEBIT	BALANCE CREDIT
19-- July 22	Balance	✓				2 4 7 96

ACCOUNT *Medicare Tax Payable*　　　　　　ACCOUNT NO. **220**

DATE	EXPLANATION	POST. REF.	DEBIT	CREDIT	BALANCE DEBIT	BALANCE CREDIT
19-- July 22	Balance	✓				5 4 44

ACCOUNT *Insurance Premiums Payable*　　　　　　ACCOUNT NO. **225**

DATE	EXPLANATION	POST. REF.	DEBIT	CREDIT	BALANCE DEBIT	BALANCE CREDIT
19-- July 22	Balance	✓				1 3 7 00

ACCOUNT *Federal Unemployment Tax Payable*　　　　　　ACCOUNT NO. **235**

DATE	EXPLANATION	POST. REF.	DEBIT	CREDIT	BALANCE DEBIT	BALANCE CREDIT
19-- July 8	Balance	✓				3 0 71
15		G 14		1 6 43		4 7 14
22		G 14		1 4 36		6 1 50

ACCOUNT *State Unemployment Tax Payable*　　　　　　ACCOUNT NO. **240**

DATE	EXPLANATION	POST. REF.	DEBIT	CREDIT	BALANCE DEBIT	BALANCE CREDIT
19-- July 8	Balance	✓				2 0 6 20
15		G 14		1 0 4 16		3 1 0 36
22		G 14		9 6 79		4 0 7 15

GENERAL LEDGER (PARTIAL)

ACCOUNT _U. S. Savings Bonds Payable_ ACCOUNT NO. _245_

DATE		EXPLANATION	POST. REF.	DEBIT	CREDIT	BALANCE DEBIT	BALANCE CREDIT
19-- July	8	Balance	✓				40 00
	15		CP18		20 00		60 00
	22		CP18		20 00		80 00

ACCOUNT _United Way Payable_ ACCOUNT NO. _250_

DATE		EXPLANATION	POST. REF.	DEBIT	CREDIT	BALANCE DEBIT	BALANCE CREDIT
19-- July	8	Balance	✓				18 00
	15		CP18		9 00		27 00
	22		CP18		9 00		36 00

ACCOUNT _Payroll Tax Expense_ ACCOUNT NO. _620_

DATE		EXPLANATION	POST. REF.	DEBIT	CREDIT	BALANCE DEBIT	BALANCE CREDIT
19-- July	8	Balance	✓			5689 20	
	15		G14	269 41		5958 61	
	22		G14	266 17		6224 78	

ACCOUNT _Salaries Expense_ ACCOUNT NO. _630_

DATE		EXPLANATION	POST. REF.	DEBIT	CREDIT	BALANCE DEBIT	BALANCE CREDIT
19-- July	15	Balance	✓			43947 39	
	22		CP18	1963 14		45910 53	

21 Accounting for Cash Funds

Name _____

Date _____ Class _____

Total Points: 41   Student's Score _____

Part 1   Accounting Vocabulary (6 points)

Directions: Using terms from the following list, complete the sentences below. Write the letter of the term you have chosen in the space provided.

A. change fund   **D.** petty cashier   **F.** petty cash requisition
B. petty cash disbursement   **E.** petty cash register   **G.** petty cash voucher
C. petty cash fund

Answer

_____F_____   **0.** The form used for requesting money to replenish the petty cash fund is a __?__ .

_____   **1.** A __?__ consists of varying denominations of bills and coins and is used to make change in cash transactions.

_____   **2.** Cash that is kept on hand by a business for making small, incidental cash payments is called a __?__ .

_____   **3.** A __?__ is a proof of payment from the petty cash fund.

_____   **4.** The person responsible for handling the petty cash fund is the __?__ .

_____   **5.** Any payment from the petty cash fund is called a __?__ .

_____   **6.** A __?__ is a record of all disbursements made from the petty cash fund.

Part 2   Examining Cash Funds (8 points)

Directions: For each of the following, select the choice that is the most suitable. Write your answer in the space provided.

Answer

_____A_____   **0.** The Change Fund account is listed on the chart of accounts as a(n) (A) asset, (B) liability, (C) revenue account, (D) expense.

_____   **1.** Which of the following businesses would probably **not** have a change fund? (A) drugstore, (B) supermarket, (C) lawyer's office, (D) newsstand.

_____   **2.** A cash proof for the change fund should be prepared at the end of the (A) accounting period, (B) month, (C) day, (D) week.

_____   **3.** Cash Short and Over is classified as a(n) (A) liability, (B) temporary owner's equity account, (C) expense, (D) revenue account.

_____   **4.** The Petty Cash Fund account is debited (A) every time the fund is replenished, (B) when the fund is established, (C) when the amount of money in the fund is increased, (D) B and C.

_____   **5.** The petty cash fund is replenished (A) when its balance reaches the minimum amount, (B) at the end of each day, (C) at the end of the fiscal period, (D) A and C.

_____   **6.** The Petty Cash Fund account is a(n) (A) expense account, (B) revenue account, (C) asset account, (D) owner's equity account.

_____   **7.** In business, cash overages are (A) revenue, (B) expenses, (C) assets, (D) liabilities.

_____   **8.** Cash shortages or overages are recorded in the (A) cash payments journal, (B) cash receipts journal, (C) general journal, (D) A and B.

Part 3   Accounting for Cash Funds (15 points)

Directions: Read each of the following statements to determine whether the statement is true or false. Write your answer in the space provided.

Answer

_____True_____   **0.** The size of the petty cash fund is determined by the needs of the business.

_____   **1.** The amount of cash sales for the day is taken from the cash register tape and entered on the cash proof form.

_____   **2.** At the end of the fiscal period, the balance of the Cash Short and Over account is closed directly into Retained Earnings.

_____   **3.** Replenishing the petty cash fund increases the fund's original balance.

_____   **4.** The salesclerk usually counts the cash in the drawer, verifies its accuracy, and signs the cash proof form.

_____   **5.** Cash shortages are liabilities and are debited to the Cash Short and Over account.

_____   **6.** The size of the petty cash fund will not change unless the business finds that it needs more or less than its original estimate.

_____   **7.** The Change Fund account is debited each time the fund is replenished.

_____   **8.** Some businesses that have a petty cash fund do not use a petty cash register.

_____   **9.** A cash proof is prepared to verify that the amount of cash in the cash register drawer is equal to the total cash sales for the day.

_____   **10.** Cash overages are revenue and are recorded as credits to the Sales account.

_____   **11.** Businesses that use a petty cash envelope for recording petty cash disbursements use a new petty cash envelope for each period's disbursements.

_____   **12.** The amounts paid out of the petty cash fund must be journalized and recorded in the appropriate general ledger accounts when the petty cash fund is replenished.

_____   **13.** The petty cash register is considered an accounting journal because all amounts are posted from this register to general ledger accounts.

_____   **14.** The balance of the cash from the cash register drawer is deposited in the business's checking account after the cash in the cash register drawer is counted and the change fund is set aside.

_____   **15.** The entry to establish the petty cash fund is recorded in the cash payments journal.

Part 4   Analyzing Cash Funds Transactions (12 points)

Directions: Using the following list of account titles, determine the account titles to be debited and credited for the transactions below.

A. Cash in Bank   **D.** Supplies   **G.** Miscellaneous Expense
B. Change Fund   **E.** Cash Short and Over
C. Petty Cash Fund   **F.** Delivery Expense

	Debit	Credit
0. Established a change fund.	B	A
1. Recorded a cash overage in the change fund.		
2. Established the petty cash fund.		
3. Replenished the petty cash fund; petty cash vouchers were for supplies, delivery expenses, and miscellaneous expenses.		
4. Increased the petty cash fund.		
5. Recorded a cash shortage in the petty cash fund.		
6. Decreased the change fund.		

Exercise 21-1, Page 478

CASH PROOF

Date _____

Cash Register No. _____

Total cash sales (from
  cash register tape) $ _____

Cash in drawer $ _____

Less change fund   _____

Net cash received   _____

Cash short   _____

Cash over   _____

Salesclerk   _____

Supervisor   _____

Exercise 21-2, Page 479

Date	Cash Sales	Sales Tax	Total Sales Amount	Cash in Drawer	Net Cash Received	Cash Short (−) or Cash Over (+)
2/11	$183.50	$ 7.34		$315.84		
2/12	199.75	7.99		332.49		
2/13	206.10	8.24		338.34		
2/14	223.15	8.93		358.18		
2/15	234.30	9.37		366.62		
2/16	288.90	11.56		435.46		

Exercise 21-3, Page 479

RIDDLE'S CARD SHOP   PETTY CASH VOUCHER

No. 13   Date _____

Paid to _____ $ _____

For _____

Account _____

Approved by   Payment received by

_____   _____

Exercise 21-4, Page 479

Date	Total Petty Cash Payments	Reconciled Petty Cash Balance	Cash Short (−) or Cash Over (+)	Amount of Replenishment Check

(2) _____

Problem 21-1, Page 479

CASH PAYMENTS JOURNAL

DATE	DOC. NO.	ACCOUNT TITLE	POST. REF.	GENERAL DEBIT	GENERAL CREDIT	ACCOUNTS PAYABLE DEBIT	PURCHASES DISCOUNTS CREDIT	CASH IN BANK CREDIT	
									1
									2
									3
									4
									5
									6
									7
									8
									9
									10

CASH RECEIPTS JOURNAL

DATE	DOC. NO.	ACCOUNT TITLE	POST. REF.	GENERAL DEBIT	GENERAL CREDIT	SALES CREDIT	SALES TAX PAYABLE CREDIT	ACCOUNTS RECEIVABLE CREDIT	CASH IN BANK DEBIT	
										1
										2
										3
										4
										5
										6
										7
										8
										9
										10

CASH PROOF

Date _____

Cash Register No. _____

Total cash sales (from
  cash register tape) $ _____

Cash in drawer $ _____

Less change fund   _____

Net cash received   _____

Cash short   _____

Cash over   _____

Salesclerk   _____

Supervisor   _____

CASH PAYMENTS JOURNAL

PAGE _____

DATE	DOC. NO.	ACCOUNT TITLE	POST. REF.	GENERAL DEBIT	GENERAL CREDIT	ACCOUNTS PAYABLE DEBIT	PURCHASES DISCOUNTS CREDIT	CASH IN BANK CREDIT
1								
2								
3								
4								
5								
6								
7								
8								
9								
10								
11								
12								
13								
14								
15								
16								
17								
18								
19								
20								
21								
22								
23								
24								
25								
26								
27								
28								

CASH PAYMENTS JOURNAL

DATE	DOC. NO.	ACCOUNT TITLE	POST. REF.	GENERAL DEBIT	GENERAL CREDIT	ACCOUNTS PAYABLE DEBIT	PURCHASES DISCOUNTS CREDIT	CASH IN BANK CREDIT	
									1
									2
									3
									4
									5
									6
									7
									8
									9
									10
									11
									12
									13
									14
									15
									16
									17
									18
									19
									20
									21
									22
									23
									24
									25
									26
									27
									28

Problem 21-3, Page 480 (Concluded)

Voucher Number	Account Title	Amount
_____	_____	$ _____
_____	_____	_____
_____	_____	_____
_____	_____	_____
_____	_____	_____
_____	_____	_____
_____	_____	_____
_____	_____	_____
_____	_____	_____
_____	_____	_____
_____	_____	_____
	TOTAL	$ _____

Office Supplies $ _____

Advertising Expense   _____

Delivery Expense   _____

Miscellaneous Expense   _____

```
PETTY CASH REQUISITION


Accounts for which
payments were made:                          Amount




TOTAL CASH NEEDED TO
REPLENISH FUND
_____

Requested by: _____ Date _____
                 Petty Cashier

Approved by: _____ Date _____
                 Accountant

                              Check No. _____
```

PAGE _____

PETTY CASH REGISTER

DATE	VOU. NO.	EXPLANATION	PAYMENTS	OFFICE SUPPLIES	DELIVERY EXPENSE	MISC. EXPENSE	GENERAL ACCOUNT TITLE	AMOUNT
1								
2								
3								
4								
5								
6								
7								
8								
9								
10								
11								
12								
13								
14								
15								
16								
17								
18								
19								
20								
21								
22								
23								
24								
25								
26								
27								
28								

DISTRIBUTION OF PAYMENTS

Problem 21-5, Page 481

CASH PAYMENTS JOURNAL

PAGE _____

DATE	DOC. NO.	ACCOUNT TITLE	POST. REF.	GENERAL DEBIT	GENERAL CREDIT	ACCOUNTS PAYABLE DEBIT	PURCHASES DISCOUNTS CREDIT	CASH IN BANK CREDIT
1								
2								
3								
4								
5								
6								
7								
8								
9								
10								
11								
12								
13								
14								
15								
16								
17								
18								
19								
20								
21								
22								
23								
24								
25								
26								
27								
28								

PAGE _____

PETTY CASH REGISTER

DATE	VOU. NO.	EXPLANATION	PAYMENTS	OFFICE SUPPLIES	DELIVERY EXPENSE	MISC. EXPENSE	DISTRIBUTION OF PAYMENTS GENERAL ACCOUNT TITLE	AMOUNT
1								1
2								2
3								3
4								4
5								5
6								6
7								7
8								8
9								9
10								10
11								11
12								12
13								13
14								14
15								15
16								16
17								17
18								18
19								19
20								20
21								21
22								22
23								23
24								24
25								25
26								26
27								27
28								28

Problem 21-5, Page 481 (Concluded)

PETTY CASH REQUISITION

Accounts for which
payments were made: Amount

TOTAL CASH NEEDED TO
REPLENISH FUND

Requested by: _____ Date _____
                    Petty Cashier

Approved by: _____ Date _____
                    Accountant

                                    Check No. _____

Extra Form

PETTY CASH REQUISITION

Accounts for which
payments were made: Amount

TOTAL CASH NEEDED TO
REPLENISH FUND

Requested by: _____ Date _____
                    Petty Cashier

Approved by: _____ Date _____
                    Accountant

                                    Check No. _____

Problem 21-6, Page 482

PETTY CASH REGISTER

DATE	VOU. NO.	EXPLANATION	PAYMENTS	OFFICE SUPPLIES	DELIVERY EXPENSE	MISC. EXPENSE	GENERAL ACCOUNT TITLE	AMOUNT
19— July 1	—	Est. petty cash fund, CK 411 $125.00						
2	1	Shopping bags	9 45				Store Supplies	9 45
3	2	ZIP Code book	5 20			5 20		
5	3	Stamps	6 25			6 00		
6	4	Prater Delivery	3 50		3 50			
8	5	Wallpaper book	8 10				Samples Expense	9 10
10	6	Typing paper	3 60	3 60				
10	7	Newspaper ad	7 50			7 50		
11	8	Coffee pot filters	2 10	2 10				
13	9	Writing tablets	8 93	8 39				
14	10	Swift Carriers	5 85		5 85			
19	11	Void						
19	12	Postage due				2 10		
21	13	Prater Delivery	3 50		3 50			
24	14	Town Taxi	7 35		7 50			
26	15	Pens and pencils	6 14				Store Supplies	6 14
29	16	Newspaper ad	8 00				Advertising Expense	8 00
30	17	Typewriter ribbons	9 13	8 00				
31	18	Order booklets	7 65				Store Supplies	7 55
31		Totals	102 25	2 2 04	20 35	20 80		40 24

22 Accounting for the Depreciation of Plant and Equipment

Name _____

Date _____ Class _____

Total Points: 42   Student's Score _____

Part 1   Accounting Vocabulary (6 points)

Directions: Using terms from the following list, complete the sentences below. Write the letter of the term you have chosen in the space provided.

A. accumulated depreciation
B. book value
C. current assets

D. depreciation
E. disposal value

F. plant and equipment
G. straight-line depreciation

Answer

_____E_____ **0.** The estimated value of a plant asset at its replacement time is called __?__ .

_____ **1.** __?__ are long-lived assets that are used in the production or sale of other assets or services over several accounting periods.

_____ **2.** __?__ is a method of equally distributing the depreciation expense on a plant asset over its estimated useful life.

_____ **3.** Allocating the cost of a plant asset over the asset's useful life is called __?__ .

_____ **4.** The original cost of a plant asset less its accumulated depreciation is the __?__ .

_____ **5.** __?__ is the total amount of depreciation for a plant asset that has been recorded up to a specific point in time.

_____ **6.** __?__ are either used up or converted to cash during a one-year accounting period.

Part 2   Accounting for Depreciation (11 points)

Directions: Read each of the following statements to determine whether the statement is true or false. Write your answer in the space provided.

Answer

_____False_____ **0.** Depreciation Expense is reported on the income statement in the cost of goods sold section.

_____ **1.** The amount of depreciation taken for a plant asset is usually recorded in the accounting records at the beginning of the fiscal period.

_____ **2.** All plant assets, including land, depreciate in value.

_____ **3.** The cost of a plant asset is the price paid for the asset plus taxes, installation charges, and delivery charges.

_____ **4.** Depreciation amounts are estimates of the decrease in value or usefulness of a plant asset over a period of time.

_____ **5.** Accumulated Depreciation is reported on the balance sheet as a liability.

_____ **6.** Depreciation Expense is recorded by an adjusting entry made in the general journal.

_____ **7.** The adjusting entry for depreciation affects two accounts for each type of plant asset: Depreciation Expense and Delivery Equipment.

_____ **8.** Delivery equipment, office equipment, buildings, and land are long-lived assets because they are expected to produce benefits for the business for more than one year.

_____ **9.** The plant asset record does not list the accumulated depreciation of an asset or its book value at the end of each year.

_____ **10.** Accumulated Depreciation is classified as a contra plant asset account.

_____ **11.** Current assets include cash, merchandise, equipment, and accounts receivable.

Part 3 Analyzing the Depreciation of Equipment (9 points)

Directions: On January 3, Washington Delivery Service purchased a new delivery truck for $20,000. The delivery truck has an estimated disposal value of $3,200 and an estimated useful life of seven years. Using this information, select the answer that best completes each of the following statements. Write your answer in the space provided.

Answer

___B___ **0.** The amount that will be debited to Delivery Equipment is (A) $16,800, (B) $20,000, (C) $3,200, (D) $23,200.

_____ **1.** The estimated annual depreciation amount using the straight-line method is (A) $3,200; (B) $16,800; (C) $2,857; (D) $2,400.

_____ **2.** The estimated depreciation amount will be recorded as a debit to (A) Accumulated Depreciation — Delivery Equipment, (B) Delivery Expense, (C) Depreciation Expense — Delivery Equipment, (D) Delivery Equipment.

_____ **3.** At the end of the fiscal period, the adjusting entry for the depreciation is a (A) debit to Depreciation Expense — Delivery Equipment and a credit to Delivery Equipment, (B) debit to Depreciation Expense — Delivery Equipment and a credit to Accumulated Depreciation — Delivery Equipment, (C) debit to Accumulated Depreciation — Delivery Equipment and a credit to Depreciation Expense — Delivery Equipment, (D) debit to Delivery Equipment and a credit to Accumulated Depreciation — Delivery Equipment.

_____ **4.** After the adjusting entries are posted to the general ledger, Depreciation Expense — Delivery Equipment will have (A) a zero balance, (B) either a debit or credit balance, (C) a debit balance, (D) a credit balance.

_____ **5.** After the adjusting entries are posted, the Delivery Equipment account will have a (A) debit balance equal to the original purchase price less the amount of the accumulated depreciation, (B) debit balance for the amount of the depreciation, (C) debit balance equal to the original purchase price, (D) credit balance for the amount of the accumulated depreciation.

_____ **6.** After the closing entry is posted, the Depreciation Expense — Delivery Equipment account will have (A) a zero balance, (B) a debit balance, (C) a credit balance, (D) either a debit or credit balance.

_____ **7.** At the beginning of the next fiscal period, Accumulated Depreciation — Delivery Equipment will have (A) a debit balance, (B) a credit balance, (C) either a debit or credit balance, (D) a zero balance.

_____ **8.** The book value of the delivery truck at the end of four years is (A) $9,600, (B) $12,800, (C) $10,400, (D) $7,200.

_____ **9.** If the Delivery Equipment had been purchased on October 1 instead of January 3, the estimated depreciation for the first year would be (A) $400, (B) $1,200, (C) $200, (D) $600.

Part 4 Classifying Assets (16 points)

Directions: Using the following codes, indicate whether each of the account titles below is a current asset or plant and equipment. Also, place a check mark (√) in the space provided for the accounts that require an adjustment for depreciation at the end of the fiscal year.

C Current Asset   **P** Plant and Equipment

Account Title	Type of Asset	Depreciation Adjustment
0. Cash in Bank	C	
1. Computer Equipment		
2. Office Supplies		
3. Accounts Receivable		
4. Building		
5. Land		
6. Delivery Equipment		
7. Change Fund		
8. Store Equipment		

Exercise 22-1, Page 500

Asset	Current Asset	Plant and Equipment
Accounts Receivable	√	
Building		
Cash in Bank		
Change Fund		
Delivery Equipment		
Land		
Merchandise Inventory		
Office Equipment		
Office Furniture		
Petty Cash Fund		
Prepaid Insurance		
Store Equipment		
Supplies		

Exercise 22-2, Page 500

Plant Asset	Original Cost	Estimated Disposal Value	Estimated Amount To Be Depreciated	Estimated Useful Life	Estimated Annual Depreciation
Building	$385,000	$15,000		25 yrs.	
Calculator	150	0		3 yrs.	
Chair	360	20		5 yrs.	
Computer	4,800	200		10 yrs.	
Typewriter	1,600	100		12 yrs.	

Exercise 22-3, Page 500

Plant Asset	Estimated Amount To Be Depreciated	Estimated Annual Depreciation	Estimated First Year Depreciation
Cash register			
Computer			
Conference table			
Delivery truck			
Desk			

Exercise 22-4, Page 500

Date	Cost	Annual Depreciation	Accumulated Depreciation	Book Value
January 7	$2,360	—	—	$2,360
First year				
Second year				
Third year				
Fourth year				
Fifth year				

Problem 22-1, Page 501

PLANT ASSET RECORD

ITEM _____   GENERAL LEDGER ACCOUNT _____

SERIAL NUMBER _____   MANUFACTURER _____

PURCHASED FROM _____   EST. DISPOSAL VALUE _____

ESTIMATED LIFE _____   LOCATION _____

DEPRECIATION   DEPRECIATION   RATE OF
METHOD _____   PER YEAR _____   DEPRECIATION _____

DATE	EXPLANATION	ASSET			ACCUMULATED DEPRECIATION			BOOK VALUE
		DEBIT	CREDIT	BALANCE	DEBIT	CREDIT	BALANCE	

Problem 22-2, Page 501

GENERAL JOURNAL   PAGE _____

	DATE		DESCRIPTION	POST. REF.	DEBIT	CREDIT	
1							1
2							2
3							3
4							4
5							5
6							6
7							7
8							8
9							9
10							10
11							11
12							12
13							13
14							14
15							15
16							16
17							17
18							18
19							19
20							20
21							21
22							22
23							23
24							24
25							25
26							26
27							27
28							28
29							29
30							30
31							31
32							32
33							33
34							34
35							35
36							36
37							37
38							38

Problem 22-3, Page 501

	ACCT. NO.	ACCOUNT NAME	TRIAL BALANCE		ADJUSTMENTS	
			DEBIT	CREDIT	DEBIT	CREDIT
1	101	Cash in Bank	10000 00			
2	105	Accounts Receivable	1200 00			
3	110	Merchandise Inventory	50000 00			(a) 3690 00
4	115	Prepaid Insurance	2400 00			(b) 1200 00
5	120	Supplies	4000 00			(c) 2960 00
6	130	Office Equipment	26000 00			
7	135	Accum. Depr.- Off. Equip.		750 00		
8	140	Store Equipment	19200 00			
9	145	Accum. Depr.-Store Equip.		3600 00		
10	201	Accounts Payable		1510 00		
11	205	Sales Tax Payable		1320 00		
12	301	J. Cagle, Capital		76515 00		
13	305	J. Cagle, Withdrawals	3600 00			
14	310	Income Summary			(a) 3690 00	
15	401	Sales		56940 00		
16	405	Sales Returns & Allow.	875 00			
17	501	Purchases	21000 00			
18	505	Transportation In	310 00			
19	510	Purchases Discounts		215 00		
20	515	Purchases Returns & Allow.		1600 00		
21	601	Advertising Expense	3000 00			
22	605	Depr. Exp.-Office Equip.				
23	610	Depr. Exp.-Store Equip.				
24	615	Insurance Expense			(b) 1200 00	
25	620	Miscellaneous Expense	425 00			
26	625	Salaries Expense	6040 00			
27	630	Supplies Expense			(c) 2960 00	
28	635	Utilities Expense	1150 00			
29			149200 00	149200 00		
30						
31						
32						
33						
34						
35						
36						
37						
38						

Company
Sheet
June 30, 19 — —

ADJUSTED TRIAL BALANCE		INCOME STATEMENT		BALANCE SHEET		
DEBIT	CREDIT	DEBIT	CREDIT	DEBIT	CREDIT	
						1
						2
						3
						4
						5
						6
						7
						8
						9
						10
						11
						12
						13
						14
						15
						16
						17
						18
						19
						20
						21
						22
						23
						24
						25
						26
						27
						28
						29
						30
						31
						32
						33
						34
						35
						36
						37
						38

Problem 22-4, Page 502 (Concluded)

Problem 22-5, Page 502

(1)

Date	Cost	Annual Depreciation	Accumulated Depreciation	Book Value
Purchased Aug. 1	$410,000	—	—	$410,000
First year				
Second year				

(2)

(3)

GENERAL JOURNAL

PAGE ___25___

	DATE	DESCRIPTION	POST. REF.	DEBIT	CREDIT	
1						1
2						2
3						3
4						4
5						5
6						6
7						7
8						8
9						9
10						10
11						11
12						12
13						13
14						14
15						15
16						16
17						17
18						18
19						19
20						20

Problem 22-5, Page 502 (Concluded)
(4)

ACCOUNT *Accum. Depreciation – Manufacturing Equip.*   ACCOUNT NO. __155__

DATE	EXPLANATION	POST. REF.	DEBIT	CREDIT	BALANCE DEBIT	BALANCE CREDIT

ACCOUNT *Depreciation Expense – Manufacturing Equip.*   ACCOUNT NO. __620__

DATE	EXPLANATION	POST. REF.	DEBIT	CREDIT	BALANCE DEBIT	BALANCE CREDIT

Olson Laundry
Work
For the Year Ended

	ACCT. NO.	ACCOUNT NAME	TRIAL BALANCE		ADJUSTMENTS	
			DEBIT	CREDIT	DEBIT	CREDIT
1	101	Cash in Bank	6690 00			
2	110	Laundry Supplies	3900 00			
3	115	Office Supplies	950 00			
4	120	Prepaid Insurance	600 00			
5	150	Laundry Equipment	13000 00			
6	155	Accum. Depr.-Laun. Equip.		6000 00		
7	160	Dry Cleaning Equipment	32000 00			
8	165	Accum. Depr.-Dry Cl. Equip.		16000 00		
9	170	Building	160000 00			
10	175	Accum. Depr.-Building		60000 00		
11	190	Land	55000 00			
12	201	Accounts Payable		2300 00		
13	205	Federal Inc. Tax Payable				
14	301	Capital Stock		75000 00		
15	305	Retained Earnings		75250 00		
16	310	Income Summary				
17	401	Laundry Revenue		19500 00		
18	405	Dry Cleaning Revenue		58500 00		
19	501	Advertising Expense	1800 00			
20	505	Depr. Expense-Laun. Equip.				
21	510	Depr. Expense-Dry Cl. Equip.				
22	515	Depr. Expense-Building				
23	520	Insurance Expense				
24	525	Laundry Supplies Exp.				
25	530	Miscellaneous Expense	1010 00			
26	535	Office Supplies Expense				
27	540	Salaries Expense	12300 00			
28	545	Utilities Expense	15900 00			
29	550	Federal Inc. Tax Expense	4000 00			
30			312550 00	312550 00		
31						
32						
33						
34						
35						
36						
37						
38						

Service
Sheet
December 31, 19--

ADJUSTED TRIAL BALANCE		INCOME STATEMENT		BALANCE SHEET		
DEBIT	CREDIT	DEBIT	CREDIT	DEBIT	CREDIT	
						1
						2
						3
						4
						5
						6
						7
						8
						9
						10
						11
						12
						13
						14
						15
						16
						17
						18
						19
						20
						21
						22
						23
						24
						25
						26
						27
						28
						29
						30
						31
						32
						33
						34
						35
						36
						37
						38

GENERAL JOURNAL

PAGE ___16___

	DATE		DESCRIPTION	POST. REF.	DEBIT	CREDIT	
1							1
2							2
3							3
4							4
5							5
6							6
7							7
8							8
9							9
10							10
11							11
12							12
13							13
14							14
15							15
16							16
17							17
18							18
19							19
20							20
21							21
22							22
23							23
24							24
25							25
26							26
27							27
28							28
29							29
30							30
31							31
32							32
33							33
34							34
35							35
36							36
37							37
38							38

Problem 22-6, Page 502 (Continued)

GENERAL JOURNAL   PAGE _____

	DATE		DESCRIPTION	POST. REF.	DEBIT	CREDIT	
1							1
2							2
3							3
4							4
5							5
6							6
7							7
8							8
9							9
10							10
11							11
12							12
13							13
14							14
15							15
16							16
17							17
18							18
19							19
20							20
21							21
22							22
23							23
24							24
25							25
26							26
27							27
28							28
29							29
30							30
31							31
32							32
33							33
34							34
35							35
36							36
37							37
38							38

GENERAL LEDGER (PARTIAL)

ACCOUNT _Laundry Supplies_   ACCOUNT NO. 110

DATE	EXPLANATION	POST. REF.	DEBIT	CREDIT	BALANCE DEBIT	BALANCE CREDIT
19-- Dec. 31	Balance	✓			3 900 00	

ACCOUNT _Office Supplies_   ACCOUNT NO. 115

DATE	EXPLANATION	POST. REF.	DEBIT	CREDIT	BALANCE DEBIT	BALANCE CREDIT
19-- Dec. 31	Balance	✓			950 00	

ACCOUNT _Prepaid Insurance_   ACCOUNT NO. 120

DATE	EXPLANATION	POST. REF.	DEBIT	CREDIT	BALANCE DEBIT	BALANCE CREDIT
19-- Dec. 31	Balance	✓			6 000 00	

ACCOUNT _Accumulated Depreciation—Laundry Equip._   ACCOUNT NO. 155

DATE	EXPLANATION	POST. REF.	DEBIT	CREDIT	BALANCE DEBIT	BALANCE CREDIT
19-- Dec. 31	Balance	✓				6 000 00

ACCOUNT _Accumulated Depreciation—Dry Cleaning Equip._   ACCOUNT NO. 165

DATE	EXPLANATION	POST. REF.	DEBIT	CREDIT	BALANCE DEBIT	BALANCE CREDIT
19-- Dec. 31	Balance	✓				16 000 00

ACCOUNT _Accumulated Depreciation—Building_   ACCOUNT NO. 175

DATE	EXPLANATION	POST. REF.	DEBIT	CREDIT	BALANCE DEBIT	BALANCE CREDIT
19-- Dec. 31	Balance	✓				60 000 00

Problem 22-6, Page 502 (Continued)

GENERAL LEDGER (PARTIAL)

ACCOUNT *Federal Income Tax Payable*   ACCOUNT NO. __205__

DATE	EXPLANATION	POST. REF.	DEBIT	CREDIT	BALANCE DEBIT	BALANCE CREDIT

ACCOUNT *Retained Earnings*   ACCOUNT NO. __305__

DATE	EXPLANATION	POST. REF.	DEBIT	CREDIT	BALANCE DEBIT	BALANCE CREDIT
19-- Dec. 31	Balance	✓				75 250 00

ACCOUNT *Income Summary*   ACCOUNT NO. __310__

DATE	EXPLANATION	POST. REF.	DEBIT	CREDIT	BALANCE DEBIT	BALANCE CREDIT

ACCOUNT *Laundry Revenue*   ACCOUNT NO. __401__

DATE	EXPLANATION	POST. REF.	DEBIT	CREDIT	BALANCE DEBIT	BALANCE CREDIT
19-- Dec. 31	Balance	✓				19 500 00

ACCOUNT *Dry Cleaning Revenue*   ACCOUNT NO. __405__

DATE	EXPLANATION	POST. REF.	DEBIT	CREDIT	BALANCE DEBIT	BALANCE CREDIT
19-- Dec. 31	Balance	✓				58 500 00

ACCOUNT *Advertising Expense*   ACCOUNT NO. __501__

DATE	EXPLANATION	POST. REF.	DEBIT	CREDIT	BALANCE DEBIT	BALANCE CREDIT
19-- Dec. 31	Balance	✓			1 800 00	

Problem 22-6, Page 502 (Continued)

GENERAL LEDGER (PARTIAL)

ACCOUNT *Depreciation Expense–Laundry Equipment*   ACCOUNT NO. 505

DATE	EXPLANATION	POST. REF.	DEBIT	CREDIT	BALANCE DEBIT	BALANCE CREDIT

ACCOUNT *Depreciation Expense–Dry Cleaning Equipment*   ACCOUNT NO. 510

DATE	EXPLANATION	POST. REF.	DEBIT	CREDIT	BALANCE DEBIT	BALANCE CREDIT

ACCOUNT *Depreciation Expense–Building*   ACCOUNT NO. 515

DATE	EXPLANATION	POST. REF.	DEBIT	CREDIT	BALANCE DEBIT	BALANCE CREDIT

ACCOUNT *Insurance Expense*   ACCOUNT NO. 520

DATE	EXPLANATION	POST. REF.	DEBIT	CREDIT	BALANCE DEBIT	BALANCE CREDIT

ACCOUNT *Laundry Supplies Expense*   ACCOUNT NO. 525

DATE	EXPLANATION	POST. REF.	DEBIT	CREDIT	BALANCE DEBIT	BALANCE CREDIT

ACCOUNT *Miscellaneous Expense*   ACCOUNT NO. 530

DATE	EXPLANATION	POST. REF.	DEBIT	CREDIT	BALANCE DEBIT	BALANCE CREDIT
19-- Dec. 31	Balance	✓			1 0 1 0 00	

Problem 22-6, Page 502 (Concluded)

GENERAL LEDGER (PARTIAL)

ACCOUNT _Office Supplies Expense_   ACCOUNT NO. 535

DATE	EXPLANATION	POST. REF.	DEBIT	CREDIT	BALANCE DEBIT	BALANCE CREDIT

ACCOUNT _Salaries Expense_   ACCOUNT NO. 540

DATE	EXPLANATION	POST. REF.	DEBIT	CREDIT	BALANCE DEBIT	BALANCE CREDIT
Dec. 31	Balance	✓			12 300 00	

ACCOUNT _Utilities Expense_   ACCOUNT NO. 545

DATE	EXPLANATION	POST. REF.	DEBIT	CREDIT	BALANCE DEBIT	BALANCE CREDIT
Dec. 31	Balance	✓			15 900 00	

ACCOUNT _Federal Income Tax Expense_   ACCOUNT NO. 550

DATE	EXPLANATION	POST. REF.	DEBIT	CREDIT	BALANCE DEBIT	BALANCE CREDIT
Dec. 31	Balance	✓			4 000 00	

ACCOUNT _____   ACCOUNT NO. _____

DATE	EXPLANATION	POST. REF.	DEBIT	CREDIT	BALANCE DEBIT	BALANCE CREDIT

Problem 22-7, Page 503

(1) _____

_____

_____

(2) _____

_____

(3) _____

_____

(4) _____

_____

(5) _____

_____

_____

(6) (a) _____

(b) _____

(c) _____

(d) _____

23 Accounting for Uncollectible Accounts Receivable

Name _____

Date _____ Class _____

Total Points: 39   Student's Score _____

Part 1   Accounting Vocabulary (5 points)

Directions: Using terms from the following list, complete the sentences below. Write the letter of the term you have chosen in the space provided.

A. aging of accounts receivable method
B. allowance method
C. book value of accounts receivable
D. direct write-off method
E. percentage of net sales method
F. uncollectible accounts

Answer

_____F_____ **0.** Accounts receivable accounts that cannot be collected are called __?__.

_____ **1.** The amount a business can reasonably expect to receive from all its charge customers is called the __?__.

_____ **2.** When a business determines that an actual amount is uncollectible, the __?__ is used to remove the uncollectible amount from the accounts receivable subsidiary ledger and the controlling account in the general ledger.

_____ **3.** When the __?__ is used to estimate the uncollectible amount, each customer's account is examined and classified according to its due date.

_____ **4.** When using the __?__ of estimating bad debts expense, a business assumes that a certain percentage of each year's net sales will be uncollectible.

_____ **5.** The __?__ of accounting for uncollectible accounts matches potential bad debts expenses with sales made during the same fiscal period.

Part 2   Accounting for Uncollectible Accounts Receivable (16 points)

Directions: Using the following list, analyze the transactions below. Determine the account(s) to be debited and credited. Write your answers in the space provided.

General Ledger Accounts

A. Cash in Bank
B. Accounts Receivable
C. Allowance for Uncollectible Accounts
D. Sales Tax Payable
E. Sales
F. Bad Debts Expense

Subsidiary Ledger Accounts

G. Jim Wright
H. Ti Yong

	Debit	Credit
0. Sold merchandise on account, plus sales tax, to Ti Yong.	B, H	D, E
1. Wrote off the account of Ti Yong as uncollectible using the allowance method.	_____	_____
2. Sold merchandise on account, plus sales tax, to Jim Wright.	_____	_____
3. Reinstated Ti Yong's account.	_____	_____
4. Received a check for payment on account from Ti Yong.	_____	_____
5. Wrote off Jim Wright's account as uncollectible using the direct write-off method.	_____	_____
6. Reinstated the account of Jim Wright.	_____	_____
7. Received a check from Jim Wright for payment of his account.	_____	_____
8. Estimated that 3% of the net sales would be uncollectible.	_____	_____

Part 3   **Extending Credit** (10 points)

Directions: Read each of the following statements to determine whether the statement is true or false. Write your answer in the space provided.

Answer

_____True_____   **0.** Two common methods used to estimate bad debts expense are the percentage of net sales method and the aging of accounts receivable method.

_____   **1.** When the direct write-off method is used for writing off an uncollectible account, Bad Debts Expense is the account debited for the amount of the loss.

_____   **2.** The two accounts affected by the adjusting entry for the allowance method of accounting for uncollectible accounts are Bad Debts Expense and Accounts Receivable.

_____   **3.** Before reinstating a charge customer's account, the receipt of cash to pay off the amount owed must be journalized.

_____   **4.** The book value of accounts receivable is the difference between the balance of Accounts Receivable and the balance of Allowance for Uncollectible Accounts.

_____   **5.** Businesses that sell on credit usually expect to sell more than if they accepted only cash.

_____   **6.** Allowance for Uncollectible Accounts is classified as a contra asset account and appears on the balance sheet as a deduction from Cash in Bank.

_____   **7.** Charge customers' accounts that are declared uncollectible become a liability to the business.

_____   **8.** Allowance for Uncollectible Accounts usually has a zero balance at the end of a fiscal period.

_____   **9.** Uncollectible accounts are sometimes paid at a later date by the customer whose account was written off.

_____   **10.** The two general ledger accounts affected by the direct write-off method of accounting for uncollectible accounts are Bad Debts Expense and Allowance for Uncollectible Accounts.

Part 4   **Estimating Bad Debts Expense** (8 points)

Directions: The Ramona Estevez Company uses the allowance method of handling bad debts. On June 30, before any adjustments have been recorded, the ledger contains the following balances:

Sales	$400,000	Accounts Receivable	$120,000
Sales Discounts	20,000	Allowance for Uncollectible Accounts	500
Sales Returns and Allowances	10,000	Bad Debts Expense	0

The Ramona Estevez Company estimates that the bad debt expenses for the year will be 2% of the net sales. Using this information, answer the following questions.

Answer

_____$370,000_____   **0.** The net sales for the fiscal year are __?__ .

_____   **1.** The estimated percentage of net sales that will be uncollectible is __?__ .

_____   **2.** The estimated bad debts expense for the fiscal year is __?__ .

_____   **3.** The account to be debited for the estimated bad debt amount is __?__ .

_____   **4.** After the adjusting entry is posted, the balance of the Allowance for Uncollectible Accounts account is __?__ .

_____   **5.** The account to be credited for the estimated bad debt amount is __?__ .

_____   **6.** After posting the adjusting entry, the balance of the Bad Debts Expense account is __?__ .

_____   **7.** The book value of accounts receivable after the adjusting entry is posted is __?__ .

_____   **8.** The financial statement on which Bad Debts Expense is reported is the __?__ .

Exercise 23-1, Page 523

	Direct Write-Off Method		Allowance Method	
Date	Debit	Credit	Debit	Credit
December 1	105	401	105	401

Exercise 23-2, Page 523

Company	Net Sales	Percentage of Net Sales	Bad Debts Expense
Andrews Co.		2%	
The Book Nook		1%	
Cable, Inc.		$1\frac{1}{2}\%$	
Davis, Inc.		2%	
Ever-Sharp Co.		$1\frac{1}{4}\%$	

Exercise 23-3, Page 524

Age Group	Amount	Estimated Percentage Uncollectible	Estimated Uncollectible Amount
Not yet due	$14,320	2%	
1-30 days past due	3,640	5%	
31-60 days past due	3,752	10%	
61-90 days past due	2,280	20%	
91-180 days past due	1,920	25%	
Over 180 days past due	634	60%	
Totals	$26,546		

GENERAL JOURNAL

PAGE _____

	DATE		DESCRIPTION	POST. REF.	DEBIT	CREDIT	
1							1
2							2
3							3
4							4
5							5
6							6
7							7
8							8
9							9
10							10
11							11
12							12
13							13
14							14
15							15
16							16
17							17
18							18
19							19
20							20
21							21
22							22
23							23
24							24
25							25
26							26
27							27
28							28
29							29
30							30
31							31
32							32
33							33
34							34
35							35
36							36
37							37
38							38

Problem 23-1, Page 524 (Continued)

ACCOUNTS RECEIVABLE SUBSIDIARY LEDGER (PARTIAL)

Name *Edward Cobb*
Address *10 Martin's Lane, Louisville, KY 40208*

DATE		EXPLANATION	POST. REF.	DEBIT	CREDIT	BALANCE
19-- May	16	Balance	✓			288 75

Name *Albert Olson*
Address *1145 Beal Street, Louisville, KY 40213*

DATE		EXPLANATION	POST. REF.	DEBIT	CREDIT	BALANCE
19-- June	30	Balance	✓			57 75

Name *Joan Schmidt*
Address *416 Sutton Place, Louisville, KY 40207*

DATE		EXPLANATION	POST. REF.	DEBIT	CREDIT	BALANCE
19-- June	16	Balance	✓			243 60

Name *Anna Waybright*
Address *1110 Branch Road, Louisville, KY 40203*

DATE		EXPLANATION	POST. REF.	DEBIT	CREDIT	BALANCE
19-- Dec.	24	Balance	✓			100 80

Problem 23-1, Page 524 (Concluded)

GENERAL LEDGER (PARTIAL)

ACCOUNT __Cash in Bank__   ACCOUNT NO. __101__

DATE	EXPLANATION	POST. REF.	DEBIT	CREDIT	BALANCE DEBIT	BALANCE CREDIT
19-- May 1	Balance	✓			1065016	

ACCOUNT __Accounts Receivable__   ACCOUNT NO. __110__

DATE	EXPLANATION	POST. REF.	DEBIT	CREDIT	BALANCE DEBIT	BALANCE CREDIT
19-- May 1	Balance	✓			801650	

ACCOUNT __Bad Debts Expense__   ACCOUNT NO. __605__

DATE	EXPLANATION	POST. REF.	DEBIT	CREDIT	BALANCE DEBIT	BALANCE CREDIT

Extra Form

ACCOUNT _____   ACCOUNT NO. _____

DATE	EXPLANATION	POST. REF.	DEBIT	CREDIT	BALANCE DEBIT	BALANCE CREDIT

Problem 23-2, Page 524

(1) Estimate of uncollectible accounts: $ _____

(2)

GENERAL JOURNAL   PAGE _____

	DATE	DESCRIPTION	POST. REF.	DEBIT	CREDIT	
1						1
2						2
3						3
4						4
5						5

(3)

GENERAL LEDGER (PARTIAL)

ACCOUNT *Allowance for Uncollectible Accounts*   ACCOUNT NO. *107*

DATE	EXPLANATION	POST. REF.	DEBIT	CREDIT	BALANCE DEBIT	BALANCE CREDIT
19-- Dec. 1	Balance	✓				400000

ACCOUNT *Bad Debts Expense*   ACCOUNT NO. *605*

DATE	EXPLANATION	POST. REF.	DEBIT	CREDIT	BALANCE DEBIT	BALANCE CREDIT

(4) Book value of accounts receivable: $ _____

Problem 23-3, Page 525

GENERAL JOURNAL

PAGE _____

	DATE	DESCRIPTION	POST. REF.	DEBIT	CREDIT	
1						1
2						2
3						3
4						4
5						5
6						6
7						7
8						8
9						9
10						10
11						11
12						12
13						13
14						14
15						15
16						16
17						17
18						18
19						19
20						20
21						21
22						22
23						23
24						24
25						25
26						26
27						27
28						28
29						29

ACCOUNTS RECEIVABLE SUBSIDIARY LEDGER (PARTIAL)

Name *King Company*

Address *416 West Fourth Street, St. Paul, MN 55102*

DATE	EXPLANATION	POST. REF.	DEBIT	CREDIT	BALANCE
19— July 27	Balance	✓			8 4 0 00

Problem 23-3, Page 525 (Continued)

ACCOUNTS RECEIVABLE SUBSIDIARY LEDGER (PARTIAL)

Name _Roger Nagel_

Address _1416 Hennepin Avenue, Minneapolis, MN 55401_

DATE	EXPLANATION	POST. REF.	DEBIT	CREDIT	BALANCE
19-- May 30	Balance	✓			262 50

Name _Tom Pernell_

Address _1300 Nicollet Avenue, Minneapolis, MN 55403_

DATE	EXPLANATION	POST. REF.	DEBIT	CREDIT	BALANCE
19-- Apr. 14	Balance	✓			593 25

Name _Stull, Inc._

Address _515 Marquette Avenue, Minneapolis, MN 55402_

DATE	EXPLANATION	POST. REF.	DEBIT	CREDIT	BALANCE
19-- Dec. 28	Balance	✓			945 00

Name _Zeron Company_

Address _550 Capital Boulevard, St. Paul, MN 55103_

DATE	EXPLANATION	POST. REF.	DEBIT	CREDIT	BALANCE
19-- Nov. 30	Balance	✓			131 25
19-- Nov. 10	Written off as uncollectible	G6		131 25	—

GENERAL LEDGER (PARTIAL)

ACCOUNT *Cash in Bank*   ACCOUNT NO. 101

DATE	EXPLANATION	POST. REF.	DEBIT	CREDIT	BALANCE DEBIT	BALANCE CREDIT
19-- Jan. 1	Balance	✓			9306 54	

ACCOUNT *Accounts Receivable*   ACCOUNT NO. 105

DATE	EXPLANATION	POST. REF.	DEBIT	CREDIT	BALANCE DEBIT	BALANCE CREDIT
19-- Jan. 1	Balance	✓			23102 00	

ACCOUNT *Allowance for Uncollectible Accounts*   ACCOUNT NO. 110

DATE	EXPLANATION	POST. REF.	DEBIT	CREDIT	BALANCE DEBIT	BALANCE CREDIT
19-- Jan. 1	Balance	✓				3164 00

ACCOUNT *Income Summary*   ACCOUNT NO. 310

DATE	EXPLANATION	POST. REF.	DEBIT	CREDIT	BALANCE DEBIT	BALANCE CREDIT

ACCOUNT *Bad Debts Expense*   ACCOUNT NO. 605

DATE	EXPLANATION	POST. REF.	DEBIT	CREDIT	BALANCE DEBIT	BALANCE CREDIT

Problem 23-3, Page 525 (Concluded)

Problem 23-4, Page 525

(1)

Customer Name	Total Amount Owed	Not Yet Due	Days Past Due				
			1-30 Days	31-60 Days	61-90 Days	91-180 Days	Over 180
N. Bellis	$ 722	$ 722					
G. Buresh	1,362		$ 761		$601		
S. Garfield	209	209					
B. Jackson	449		132	$317			
P. Kramer	271					$271	
E. McGarrell	1,066	640		426			
B. O'Brien	48					48	
S. Schoenle	1,998	1,998					
D. Southworth	790	428	362				
S. Wright	296						$296
Totals							

(2)

Age Group	Amount	Estimated Percentage Uncollectible	Estimated Uncollectible Amount
Not yet due		2%	
1-30 days past due		4%	
31-60 days past due		20%	
61-90 days past due		30%	
91-180 days past due		45%	
Over 180 days past due		60%	
Totals			

Name _____ **Date** _____ **Class** _____

Problem 23-4, Page 525 (Concluded)

3)

GENERAL JOURNAL   PAGE _____

	DATE	DESCRIPTION	POST. REF.	DEBIT	CREDIT	
1						1
2						2
3						3
4						4
5						5
6						6
7						7
8						8
9						9
10						10

4)

GENERAL LEDGER (PARTIAL)

ACCOUNT *Accounts Receivable*   ACCOUNT NO. 105

DATE	EXPLANATION	POST. REF.	DEBIT	CREDIT	BALANCE DEBIT	BALANCE CREDIT
Dec. 31	Balance	✓			7211 00	

ACCOUNT *Allowance for Uncollectible Accounts*   ACCOUNT NO. 110

DATE	EXPLANATION	POST. REF.	DEBIT	CREDIT	BALANCE DEBIT	BALANCE CREDIT
Dec. 31	Balance	✓				142 00

ACCOUNT *Bad Debts Expense*   ACCOUNT NO. 610

DATE	EXPLANATION	POST. REF.	DEBIT	CREDIT	BALANCE DEBIT	BALANCE CREDIT

Book value of accounts receivable: $ _____

	ACCT. NO.	ACCOUNT NAME	TRIAL BALANCE DEBIT	TRIAL BALANCE CREDIT	ADJUSTMENTS DEBIT	ADJUSTMENTS CREDIT
1	101	Cash in Bank	21633 50			
2	105	Accounts Receivable	10168 45			
3	107	Allow. for Uncoll. Accts.		400 00		
4	110	Merchandise Inventory	39391 75			(b) 3630 25
5	115	Supplies	2875 00			(c) 1900 00
6	120	Prepaid Insurance	3100 00			(d) 2000 00
7	150	Equipment	30000 00			
8	152	Accum. Depr.- Equipment		3610 00		(e) 500 00
9	201	Accounts Payable		3960 00		
10	205	Fed. Inc. Tax Payable				(f) 1806 00
11	210	Sales Tax Payable		613 10		
12	301	Capital Stock		40000 00		
13	305	Retained Earnings		9764 15		
14	310	Income Summary			(b) 3630 25	
15	401	Sales		152875 20		
16	405	Sales Returns & Allow.	3585 00			
17	501	Purchases	81860 00			
18	505	Transportation In	3956 00			
19	510	Purchases Discounts		740 00		
20	515	Purchases Returns & Allow.		1221 00		
21	601	Bad Debts Expense				
22	605	Bank Card Fees Expense	452 75			
23	610	Depr. Expense-Equipment			(e) 500 00	
24	615	Insurance Expense			(d) 2000 00	
25	620	Miscellaneous Expense	730 00			
26	625	Rent Expense	9600 00			
27	630	Supplies Expense			(c) 1900 00	
28	635	Utilities Expense	2081 00			
29	640	Fed. Inc. Tax Expense	3750 00		(f) 1806 00	
30			213183 45	213183 45		
31						
32						
33						
34						
35						
36						
37						
38						

Products, Inc.
Sheet
December 31, 19--

| ADJUSTED TRIAL BALANCE | | INCOME STATEMENT | | BALANCE SHEET | | |
DEBIT	CREDIT	DEBIT	CREDIT	DEBIT	CREDIT	
						1
						2
						3
						4
						5
						6
						7
						8
						9
						10
						11
						12
						13
						14
						15
						16
						17
						18
						19
						20
						21
						22
						23
						24
						25
						26
						27
						28
						29
						30
						31
						32
						33
						34
						35
						36
						37
						38

Problem 23-5, Page 526 (Continued)

Problem 23-5, Page 526 (Continued)
(4), (6)

GENERAL JOURNAL

	DATE		DESCRIPTION	POST. REF.	DEBIT	CREDIT	
1							1
2							2
3							3
4							4
5							5
6							6
7							7
8							8
9							9
10							10
11							11
12							12
13							13
14							14
15							15
16							16
17							17
18							18
19							19
20							20
21							21
22							22
23							23
24							24
25							25
26							26
27							27
28							28
29							29
30							30
31							31
32							32
33							33
34							34
35							35
36							36
37							37
38							38

Problem 23-5, Page 526 (Continued)

GENERAL LEDGER

ACCOUNT *Cash in Bank*   ACCOUNT NO. 101

DATE		EXPLANATION	POST. REF.	DEBIT	CREDIT	BALANCE DEBIT	BALANCE CREDIT
19-- Dec.	31	Balance	✓			21 633 50	

ACCOUNT *Accounts Receivable*   ACCOUNT NO. 105

DATE		EXPLANATION	POST. REF.	DEBIT	CREDIT	BALANCE DEBIT	BALANCE CREDIT
19-- Dec.	31	Balance	✓			10 168 45	

ACCOUNT *Allowance for Uncollectible Accounts*   ACCOUNT NO. 107

DATE		EXPLANATION	POST. REF.	DEBIT	CREDIT	BALANCE DEBIT	BALANCE CREDIT
19-- Dec.	31	Balance	✓				400 00

ACCOUNT *Merchandise Inventory*   ACCOUNT NO. 110

DATE		EXPLANATION	POST. REF.	DEBIT	CREDIT	BALANCE DEBIT	BALANCE CREDIT
19-- Dec.	31	Balance	✓			39 391 75	

ACCOUNT *Supplies*   ACCOUNT NO. 115

DATE		EXPLANATION	POST. REF.	DEBIT	CREDIT	BALANCE DEBIT	BALANCE CREDIT
19-- Dec.	31	Balance	✓			2 875 00	

ACCOUNT *Prepaid Insurance*   ACCOUNT NO. 120

DATE		EXPLANATION	POST. REF.	DEBIT	CREDIT	BALANCE DEBIT	BALANCE CREDIT
19-- Dec.	31	Balance	✓			3 100 00	

Problem 23-5, Page 526 (Continued)

GENERAL LEDGER

ACCOUNT *Equipment*   ACCOUNT NO. 150

DATE	EXPLANATION	POST. REF.	DEBIT	CREDIT	BALANCE DEBIT	BALANCE CREDIT
Dec. 31	Balance	✓			30 000 00	

ACCOUNT *Accumulated Depreciation – Equipment*   ACCOUNT NO. 152

DATE	EXPLANATION	POST. REF.	DEBIT	CREDIT	BALANCE DEBIT	BALANCE CREDIT
Dec. 31	Balance	✓				3 610 00

ACCOUNT *Accounts Payable*   ACCOUNT NO. 201

DATE	EXPLANATION	POST. REF.	DEBIT	CREDIT	BALANCE DEBIT	BALANCE CREDIT
Dec. 31	Balance	✓				3 960 00

ACCOUNT *Federal Income Tax Payable*   ACCOUNT NO. 205

DATE	EXPLANATION	POST. REF.	DEBIT	CREDIT	BALANCE DEBIT	BALANCE CREDIT

ACCOUNT *Sales Tax Payable*   ACCOUNT NO. 210

DATE	EXPLANATION	POST. REF.	DEBIT	CREDIT	BALANCE DEBIT	BALANCE CREDIT
Dec. 31	Balance	✓				613 10

ACCOUNT *Capital Stock*   ACCOUNT NO. 301

DATE	EXPLANATION	POST. REF.	DEBIT	CREDIT	BALANCE DEBIT	BALANCE CREDIT
Dec. 31	Balance	✓				40 000 00

Problem 23-5, Page 526 (Continued)

GENERAL LEDGER

ACCOUNT _Retained Earnings_   ACCOUNT NO. 305

DATE		EXPLANATION	POST. REF.	DEBIT	CREDIT	BALANCE DEBIT	BALANCE CREDIT
19-- Dec.	31	Balance	✓				9764 15

ACCOUNT _Income Summary_   ACCOUNT NO. 310

DATE	EXPLANATION	POST. REF.	DEBIT	CREDIT	BALANCE DEBIT	BALANCE CREDIT

ACCOUNT _Sales_   ACCOUNT NO. 401

DATE		EXPLANATION	POST. REF.	DEBIT	CREDIT	BALANCE DEBIT	BALANCE CREDIT
19-- Dec.	31	Balance	✓				152875 20

ACCOUNT _Sales Returns and Allowances_   ACCOUNT NO. 405

DATE		EXPLANATION	POST. REF.	DEBIT	CREDIT	BALANCE DEBIT	BALANCE CREDIT
19-- Dec.	31	Balance	✓			3585 00	

ACCOUNT _Purchases_   ACCOUNT NO. 501

DATE		EXPLANATION	POST. REF.	DEBIT	CREDIT	BALANCE DEBIT	BALANCE CREDIT
19-- Dec.	31	Balance	✓			81860 00	

ACCOUNT _Transportation In_   ACCOUNT NO. 505

DATE		EXPLANATION	POST. REF.	DEBIT	CREDIT	BALANCE DEBIT	BALANCE CREDIT
19-- Dec.	31	Balance	✓			3956 00	

GENERAL LEDGER

ACCOUNT _Purchases Discounts_   ACCOUNT NO. __510__

DATE		EXPLANATION	POST. REF.	DEBIT	CREDIT	BALANCE DEBIT	BALANCE CREDIT
19-- Dec.	31	Balance	✓				740 00

ACCOUNT _Purchases Returns and Allowances_   ACCOUNT NO. __515__

DATE		EXPLANATION	POST. REF.	DEBIT	CREDIT	BALANCE DEBIT	BALANCE CREDIT
19-- Dec.	31	Balance	✓				1 221 00

ACCOUNT _Bad Debts Expense_   ACCOUNT NO. __601__

DATE		EXPLANATION	POST. REF.	DEBIT	CREDIT	BALANCE DEBIT	BALANCE CREDIT

ACCOUNT _Bank Card Fees Expense_   ACCOUNT NO. __605__

DATE		EXPLANATION	POST. REF.	DEBIT	CREDIT	BALANCE DEBIT	BALANCE CREDIT
19-- Dec.	31	Balance	✓			452 75	

ACCOUNT _Depreciation Expense – Equipment_   ACCOUNT NO. __610__

DATE		EXPLANATION	POST. REF.	DEBIT	CREDIT	BALANCE DEBIT	BALANCE CREDIT

ACCOUNT _Insurance Expense_   ACCOUNT NO. __615__

DATE		EXPLANATION	POST. REF.	DEBIT	CREDIT	BALANCE DEBIT	BALANCE CREDIT

Name _____ Date _____ Class _____

Problem 23-5, Page 526 (Concluded)

GENERAL LEDGER

ACCOUNT _Miscellaneous Expense_   ACCOUNT NO. _620_

DATE	EXPLANATION	POST. REF.	DEBIT	CREDIT	BALANCE DEBIT	BALANCE CREDIT
19-- Dec. 31	Balance	✓			730 00	

ACCOUNT _Rent Expense_   ACCOUNT NO. _625_

DATE	EXPLANATION	POST. REF.	DEBIT	CREDIT	BALANCE DEBIT	BALANCE CREDIT
19-- Dec. 31	Balance	✓			9600 00	

ACCOUNT _Supplies Expense_   ACCOUNT NO. _630_

DATE	EXPLANATION	POST. REF.	DEBIT	CREDIT	BALANCE DEBIT	BALANCE CREDIT

ACCOUNT _Utilities Expense_   ACCOUNT NO. _635_

DATE	EXPLANATION	POST. REF.	DEBIT	CREDIT	BALANCE DEBIT	BALANCE CREDIT
19-- Dec. 31	Balance	✓			2081 00	

ACCOUNT _Federal Income Tax Expense_   ACCOUNT NO. _640_

DATE	EXPLANATION	POST. REF.	DEBIT	CREDIT	BALANCE DEBIT	BALANCE CREDIT
19-- Dec. 31	Balance	✓			3750 00	

GENERAL JOURNAL

PAGE _____

	DATE	DESCRIPTION	POST. REF.	DEBIT	CREDIT	
1						1
2						2
3						3
4						4
5						5
6						6
7						7
8						8
9						9
10						10
11						11
12						12
13						13
14						14
15						15
16						16
17						17
18						18
19						19
20						20
21						21

Name _Terry Mahady_

Address _1145 Ridge Avenue, Lawrenceburg, IN 47025_

DATE	EXPLANATION	POST. REF.	DEBIT	CREDIT	BALANCE
19-- Jan. 1	Balance	✓			1 9 4 50

24 Accounting for Inventories

Name _____

Date _____ Class _____

Total Points: 32   Student's Score _____

Part 1   Accounting Vocabulary (8 points)

Directions: Using terms from the following list, complete the sentences below. Write the letter of the term you have chosen in the space provided.

A. conservatism
B. first in, first out method
C. last in, first out method

D. market value
E. online
F. periodic inventory system

G. perpetual inventory system
H. specific identification method
I. weighted average cost method

Answer

___D___   0. __?__ is the current price that is being charged for similar items of merchandise in the market.

_____   1. The inventory costing method under which the cost of the items on hand is determined by the average cost of all identical items purchased during the period is the __?__ .

_____   2. When a terminal or cash register is __?__ , it is linked directly to a computer and feeds data into the appropriate files controlled by the computer.

_____   3. The __?__ is the inventory costing method that assumes the last items purchased are the first items sold.

_____   4. __?__ is the accounting guideline that states a business should report its financial position in amounts that are least likely to result in an overstatement of income or property values.

_____   5. The inventory costing method that assumes the first items purchased were the first items sold is the __?__ .

_____   6. The inventory costing method under which the exact cost of each item on the inventory sheet must be determined and assigned to that item is the __?__ .

_____   7. The __?__ requires a constant, up-to-date record of merchandise on hand.

_____   8. The __?__ requires a physical count of all merchandise on hand to determine the quantity of merchandise on hand.

Part 2   Comparing Inventory Costing Methods (6 points)

Directions: Read each of the statements below and determine the inventory method that completes the statement. Write the identifying letter of your choice in the space provided.

A. first in, first out method
B. last in, first out method

C. specific identification method
D. weighted average cost method

Answer

___C___   0. The __?__ is a time-consuming process.

_____   1. The __?__ is used by businesses that have a low unit volume of merchandise with high unit prices.

_____   2. According to the __?__ , the items still on hand at the end of the fiscal period are assumed to be the last items purchased.

_____   3. The __?__ assumes that the items still on hand at the end of the period are the first ones purchased.

_____   4. The __?__ takes into account the costs of all the merchandise available for sale during the period.

_____   5. The __?__ is the most realistic costing method.

_____   6. The last in, first out method and the __?__ are based on certain assumptions about the items remaining in inventory.

Part 3   Calculating Inventory Costs (6 points)

Directions: The Lindborg Craft Shop has the following record of crewel kits for the month of April:

Beginning inventory	13 units @ $3.48 =	$ 45.24
Purchased April 4	15 units @ $3.51 =	52.65
Purchased April 9	20 units @ $3.67 =	73.40
Purchased April 14	10 units @ $3.71 =	37.10
Purchased April 26	15 units @ $3.74 =	56.10
	73	$264.49

At the end of April, there were 22 units on hand. Based on the above information, complete the following statements.

Answer

_____ $82.07 _____

0. The value of the ending inventory using the fifo method is __?__ .
1. The value of the ending inventory using the lifo method is __?__ .
2. The value of the ending inventory using the weighted average cost method is __?__ .
3. The purchase that will have the greatest impact on the weighted average cost method was made on __?__ .
4. If the lifo method is used and if the current market value of its inventory is $80.37, the Lindborg Craft Shop would report the value of its inventory at __?__ .
5. The __?__ method produces the highest value for the ending inventory.
6. The __?__ method produces the lowest value for the ending inventory.

Part 4   Choosing an Inventory Costing Method (12 points)

Directions: Read each of the following statements to determine whether the statement is true or false. Write your answer in the space provided.

Answer

_____ True _____

0. A perpetual inventory system can be established without a computer.
1. When a cash register is linked to a computer, it is said to be online.
2. The costing method used to determine the value of the ending inventory will not affect a company's gross profit on sales or net income.
3. A business may change inventory costing methods without obtaining permission from the Internal Revenue Service.
4. The market value of the merchandise on hand is always lower than the original cost.
5. The most commonly used method of determining the quantity of merchandise on hand is the perpetual inventory system.
6. A physical inventory should be conducted at least once a year.
7. The weighted average cost method is the most accurate inventory costing method.
8. A periodic inventory system provides management with continuous merchandise inventory information.
9. The specific identification method can often be used by businesses that sell large items such as automobiles.
10. When choosing an inventory costing method, a business's owner or manager should consider only the present economic conditions.
11. An inventory control system includes the quantity of merchandise on hand at a given time and the selling price of that merchandise.
12. The lower-of-cost-or-market rule for reporting inventory value allows a business to follow a conservative approach.

Name _____ Date _____ Class _____

Exercise 24-1, Page 541

3 mowers @ $94.95 = _____

4 mowers @ $96.00 = _____

2 mowers @ $97.00 = _____

<u>3</u> mowers @ $98.50 = _____

12 _____

Exercise 24-2, Page 541

_____ tablecloths @ $_____ = _____

_____ tablecloths @ $_____ = _____

29 _____

Exercise 24-3, Page 541

_____ tires @ $_____ = _____

_____ tires @ $_____ = _____

_____ tires @ $_____ = _____

38 _____

Exercise 24-4, Page 541

16 smoke detectors @ $1.98 = _____

48 smoke detectors @ $2.25 = _____

60 smoke detectors @ $2.45 = _____

24 smoke detectors @ $2.69 = _____

36 smoke detectors @ $2.62 = _____

72 smoke detectors @ $2.66 = _____

_____ _____

27 smoke detectors × $_____ = _____

Problem 24-1, Page 542

	Specific Identification Method	Fifo Method	Lifo Method	Weighted Average Cost Method
Ending Inventory	$ _____	$ _____	$ _____	$ _____

Problem 24-2, Page 542

Specific Identification

Total cameras available for sale (_____ units) $ _____

Less ending inventory (_____ units)   _____

Cost of merchandise sold (_____ units) $ _____

Fifo

Total cameras available for sale (_____ units) $ _____

Less ending inventory (_____ units)   _____

Cost of merchandise sold (_____ units) $ _____

Lifo

Total cameras available for sale (_____ units) $ _____

Less ending inventory (_____ units)   _____

Cost of merchandise sold (_____ units) $ _____

Weighted Average Cost

Total cameras available for sale (_____ units) $ _____

Less ending inventory (_____ units)   _____

Cost of merchandise sold (_____ units) $ _____

Name _____ Date _____ Class _____

Problem 24-3, Page 542

			INVENTORY RECORD			
Item No.	Item	Ending Inventory	Cost Per Unit	Current Market Value	Price To Be Used	Total Cost
1	2	3	4	5	6	7
0247	Tubes 24"	24	2.67	2.83	2.67	64.08
0391	Tubes 25"	36	2.80	2.74		
0388	Tubes 27"	21	2.91	3.05		
0379	2½" Petals	6	6.36	8.30		
0380	3" Petals	19	7.49	7.51		
0274	5" Horns	23	6.90	6.95		
0276	7" Horns	12	8.14	7.95		
0277	9" Horns	14	9.25	9.57		
0181	4" Handle Grips	18	2.06	2.52		
0193	5" Handle Grips	9	2.29	2.71		
0419	38" Chains	8	8.42	8.73		
0420	40" Chains	14	8.98	9.19		
0421	42" Chains	9	8.99	8.95		
0619	Brake Pads	98	1.49	1.41		
0799	Brake Handles	47	9.29	8.60		
0170	Brake Wire (S)	19	2.36	2.52		
0173	Brake Wire (L)	14	2.90	3.15		
0803	2" Reflectors	38	.98	1.04		
0804	4" Reflectors	10	1.19	1.40		
0249	Bike Seats	9	14.92	14.65		
0019	Spokes (Pkg.)	16	2.19	2.14		
0917	Pumps	8	7.95	8.50		
0989	Gear Wire	11	.73	.69		
					TOTAL COST	

Problem 24-4, Page 543

	Specific Identification Method	Fifo Method	Lifo Method	Weighted Average Cost Method
Net Sales	$	$	$	$
Cost of Merchandise Sold	$	$	$	$
Gross Profit on Sales	$	$	$	$

Problem 24-5, Page 543

	Fifo Method	Lifo Method	Weighted Average Cost Method
Ending Inventory	$	$	$
Cost of Merchandise Sold			

(3)
Fifo Method

Problem 24-5, Page 543 (Concluded)
(3)

Lifo Method

Weighted Average Cost Method

Problem 24-6, Page 544

	28″ bicycles	26″ bicycles	24″ bicycles	Total
Cost of merchandise available for sale	$	$	$	$
Ending inventory				
Cost of merchandise sold				

(4)

Problem 24-7, Page 544

(1)

#3845 _____   #4931 _____

#9265 _____   #4850 _____

(2)

	Item			
	3845	4931	9265	4850
Sales for the Month				
Value of Beginning Inventory				
Purchases for May				
Transportation Costs				
Purchases Returns and Allowances				
Net Purchases for May				
Goods Available for Sale				
Value of Ending Inventory				
Cost of Merchandise Sold				
Gross Profit on Sales				

Name _____

Date _____ Class _____

Total Points: 47   Student's Score _____

Part 1   Accounting Vocabulary (18 points)

Directions: Using terms from the following list, complete the sentences below. Write the letter of the term you have chosen in the space provided.

A. bank discount
B. face value
C. interest
D. interest-bearing note payable
E. interest rate
F. issue date
G. maker

H. maturity date
I. maturity value
J. non-interest-bearing note payable
K. note payable
L. note receivable
M. other expense

N. other revenue
O. payee
P. principal
Q. proceeds
R. promissory note
S. term

Answer

_____B_____   **0.** The ___?___ of a promissory note is the amount of money written on the face of the note.

_____   **1.** The date on which a note is written is called its ___?___ .

_____   **2.** The ___?___ of the note is the person or business promising to repay the principal and interest.

_____   **3.** A(n) ___?___ is a promissory note issued to a creditor or by a business to borrow money from a bank.

_____   **4.** The ___?___ is the date on which the note must be paid.

_____   **5.** The amount of interest to be charged stated as a percentage of the principal is called the ___?___ .

_____   **6.** The amount being borrowed is the ___?___ of the note.

_____   **7.** A promissory note that a business accepts from a customer who needs additional time to pay a debt is called a(n) ___?___ .

_____   **8.** ___?___ is the fee charged for the use of money.

_____   **9.** A note that requires the face value plus interest be paid on the maturity date is called a(n) ___?___ .

_____   **10.** The ___?___ is the amount of time that the borrower has to repay a promissory note.

_____   **11.** The person or business to whom a promissory note is made payable is the ___?___ .

_____   **12.** A(n) ___?___ is a written promise to pay a business or a person a certain amount of money at a specific time.

_____   **13.** The interest deducted in advance from a non-interest-bearing note payable is called the ___?___ .

_____   **14.** An expense that does not result from the normal operations of the business is called a(n) ___?___ .

_____   **15.** A promissory note from which the interest has been deducted in advance and which therefore has no interest rate stated on the note itself is called a(n) ___?___ .

_____   **16.** The amount of cash actually received by the borrower of a non-interest-bearing note payable is called the ___?___ .

_____   **17.** The ___?___ of a note is the principal plus the interest.

_____   **18.** ___?___ is revenue that a business receives or earns from activities outside the normal operations of the business.

Part 2   Examining Notes Payable and Receivable (15 points)

Directions: Read each of the following statements to determine whether the statement is true or false. Write your answer in the space provided.

Answer

___True___   **0.** Promissory notes are formal documents that provide evidence that credit was granted or received.

_____   **1.** When a non-interest-bearing note payable is paid, the interest charge is transferred from the Notes Payable account to the Interest Expense account.

_____   **2.** I = PRT is the equation for calculating interest on a promissory note.

_____   **3.** A note receivable is an asset to the business receiving the note.

_____   **4.** Discount on Notes Payable is a liability account.

_____   **5.** Interest rates are usually stated on an annual basis.

_____   **6.** The maturity value of a non-interest-bearing note payable is the same as its face value.

_____   **7.** Notes Receivable is classified as a contra asset account, and its normal balance is a credit.

_____   **8.** Both the term and the issue date are needed to determine the maturity date of a note.

_____   **9.** Borrowing periods of less than one year cannot be used in calculating interest.

_____   **10.** The interest on a 12.5%, $3,500.00 promissory note for two years is $437.50.

_____   **11.** On interest-bearing notes, the face value and the principal are the same.

_____   **12.** A business may not issue a note payable to borrow money from a bank.

_____   **13.** A non-interest-bearing note payable is the same as an interest-free note.

_____   **14.** Interest income is an example of other revenue and is reported separately on the income statement.

_____   **15.** The payment of a non-interest-bearing note payable and the recognition of the interest expense are always recorded with two separate journal entries in the cash payments journal and in the general journal.

Part 3   Analyzing Transactions Affecting Notes Payable and Receivable (14 points)

Directions: Using the following account titles, analyze the transactions below. Determine the account(s) to be debited and credited. Write your answers in the space provided.

A. Cash in Bank   **D.** Notes Payable   **G.** Sales
B. Accounts Receivable   **E.** Discount on Notes Payable   **H.** Interest Expense
C. Notes Receivable   **F.** Interest Income

	Debit	Credit
0. Sold merchandise on account to a customer.	B	G
1. Received an interest-bearing note from a customer for payment on account.	_____	_____
2. Issued an interest-bearing note payable to the bank for cash.	_____	_____
3. Received a check for the payment of the interest-bearing note from the customer.	_____	_____
4. Issued a non-interest-bearing note to the bank for cash.	_____	_____
5. Wrote a check to the bank for payment of the interest-bearing note.	_____	_____
6. Wrote a check to the bank for payment on the non-interest-bearing note.	_____	_____
7. Received the interest due on a note receivable and renewed the note for 90 days.	_____	_____

Exercise 25-1, Page 563

	Issue Date	Term	Maturity Date
1.	November 18	60 days	_____
2.	August 3	90 days	_____
3.	July 22	120 days	_____
4.	February 5	3 months	_____
5.	April 28	9 months	_____

Exercise 25-2, Page 563

	Principal	Interest Rate	Term	Interest
1.	$ 600	15%	90 days	$ _____
2.	3,500	12%	60 days	_____
3.	9,600	9%	4 months	_____
4.	2,500	10%	180 days	_____
5.	1,500	11½%	6 months	_____

Exercise 25-3, Page 563

	Principal	Interest Rate	Term	Interest	Maturity Value
1.	$ 900	9%	80 days	$ _____	$ _____
2.	1,200	12%	60 days	_____	_____
3.	3,250	10%	90 days	_____	_____
4.	2,430	15%	2 months	_____	_____
5.	210	8%	3 months	_____	_____

Exercise 25-4, Page 563

	Face Value	Term	Discount Rate	Bank Discount	Proceeds
1.	$ 300	60 days	12%	$ _____	$ _____
2.	3,840	90 days	9%	_____	_____
3.	2,100	4 months	11%	_____	_____
4.	5,000	7 months	7%	_____	_____
5.	800	5 months	8%	_____	_____

CASH RECEIPTS JOURNAL

PAGE 22

DATE	DOC. NO.	ACCOUNT TITLE	POST. REF.	GENERAL DEBIT	GENERAL CREDIT	SALES CREDIT	SALES TAX PAYABLE CREDIT	ACCOUNTS RECEIVABLE CREDIT	CASH IN BANK DEBIT	
										1
										2
										3
										4
										5
										6
										7
										8
										9
										10

CASH PAYMENTS JOURNAL

PAGE 26

DATE	DOC. NO.	ACCOUNT TITLE	POST. REF.	GENERAL DEBIT	GENERAL CREDIT	ACCOUNTS PAYABLE DEBIT	PURCHASES DISCOUNTS CREDIT	CASH IN BANK CREDIT	
									1
									2
									3
									4
									5
									6
									7
									8
									9
									10

Problem 25-2, Page 564

PAGE __14__

CASH RECEIPTS JOURNAL

DATE	DOC. NO.	ACCOUNT TITLE	POST. REF.	GENERAL DEBIT	GENERAL CREDIT	SALES CREDIT	SALES TAX PAYABLE CREDIT	ACCOUNTS RECEIVABLE CREDIT	CASH IN BANK DEBIT

PAGE __16__

CASH PAYMENTS JOURNAL

DATE	DOC. NO.	ACCOUNT TITLE	POST. REF.	GENERAL DEBIT	GENERAL CREDIT	ACCOUNTS PAYABLE DEBIT	PURCHASES DISCOUNTS CREDIT	CASH IN BANK CREDIT

GENERAL JOURNAL

PAGE _10_

DATE	DESCRIPTION	POST. REF.	DEBIT	CREDIT

CASH RECEIPTS JOURNAL

PAGE _29_

DATE	DOC. NO.	ACCOUNT TITLE	POST. REF.	GENERAL DEBIT	GENERAL CREDIT	SALES CREDIT	SALES TAX PAYABLE CREDIT	ACCOUNTS RECEIVABLE CREDIT	CASH IN BANK DEBIT

Problem 25-4, Page 564

PAGE _____

CASH RECEIPTS JOURNAL

DATE	DOC. NO.	ACCOUNT TITLE	POST. REF.	GENERAL DEBIT	GENERAL CREDIT	SALES CREDIT	SALES TAX PAYABLE CREDIT	ACCOUNTS RECEIVABLE CREDIT	CASH IN BANK DEBIT
									1
									2
									3
									4
									5
									6
									7
									8
									9
									10

PAGE _____

CASH PAYMENTS JOURNAL

DATE	DOC. NO.	ACCOUNT TITLE	POST. REF.	GENERAL DEBIT	GENERAL CREDIT	ACCOUNTS PAYABLE DEBIT	PURCHASES DISCOUNTS CREDIT	CASH IN BANK CREDIT
								1
								2
								3
								4
								5
								6
								7
								8
								9
								10

Problem 25-4, Page 564 (Concluded)

GENERAL JOURNAL   PAGE _____

	DATE	DESCRIPTION	POST. REF.	DEBIT	CREDIT	
1						1
2						2
3						3
4						4
5						5
6						6
7						7
8						8
9						9
10						10
11						11
12						12
13						13
14						14
15						15
16						16
17						17

Problem 25-5, Page 565

GENERAL JOURNAL   PAGE _____

	DATE	DESCRIPTION	POST. REF.	DEBIT	CREDIT	
1						1
2						2
3						3
4						4
5						5
6						6
7						7
8						8
9						9
10						10
11						11
12						12
13						13
14						14
15						15
16						16
17						17

Problem 25-5, Page 565 (Concluded)

CASH RECEIPTS JOURNAL

DATE	DOC. NO.	ACCOUNT TITLE	POST. REF.	GENERAL DEBIT	GENERAL CREDIT	SALES CREDIT	SALES TAX PAYABLE CREDIT	ACCOUNTS RECEIVABLE CREDIT	CASH IN BANK DEBIT
									1
									2
									3
									4
									5
									6
									7
									8
									9
									10

CASH PAYMENTS JOURNAL

DATE	DOC. NO.	ACCOUNT TITLE	POST. REF.	GENERAL DEBIT	GENERAL CREDIT	ACCOUNTS PAYABLE DEBIT	PURCHASES DISCOUNTS CREDIT	CASH IN BANK CREDIT
								1
								2
								3
								4
								5
								6
								7
								8
								9
								10

Problem 25-6, Page 565

	Maturity Date	Interest	
		Current Year	Following Year
1.	_____	_____	_____
2.	_____	_____	_____
3.	_____	_____	_____
4.	_____	_____	_____
5.	_____	_____	_____
6.	_____	_____	_____
7.	_____	_____	_____
8.	_____	_____	_____
9.	_____	_____	_____
10.	_____	_____	_____

Problem 25-7, Page 566

GENERAL JOURNAL   PAGE _____

	DATE	DESCRIPTION	POST. REF.	DEBIT	CREDIT	
1						1
2						2
3						3
4						4
5						5
6						6
7						7
8						8
9						9
10						10
11						11
12						12
13						13
14						14
15						15
16						16
17						17
18						18
19						19
20						20

Name _____

Date _____ Class _____

Total Points: 36   Student's Score _____

Part 1   Accounting Vocabulary (3 points)

Directions: Using terms from the following list, complete the sentences below. Write the letter of the term you have chosen in the space provided.

A. mutual agency
B. partnership

C. partnership agreement

D. statement of changes in partners' equity

Answer

_____B_____   **0.** An association of two or more persons to operate a business for profit is called a __?__ .

_____   **1.** Within a partnership, the relationship that allows any partner to enter into agreements that are binding on all other partners is called __?__ .

_____   **2.** The financial statement that reports the changes in each partner's capital account resulting from the business operations is called the __?__ .

_____   **3.** A __?__ is a written document that sets out the terms under which a partnership will operate.

Part 2   Partnerships (11 points)

Directions: Read each of the following statements to determine whether the statement is true or false. Write your answer in the space provided.

Answer

_____True_____   **0.** Withdrawals within a partnership are recorded the same way as are the withdrawals of the owner of a sole proprietorship.

_____   **1.** When a partner invests assets in the partnership, he or she retains personal rights of ownership.

_____   **2.** A partnership may be formed through an oral agreement between two or more individuals.

_____   **3.** The amount of the withdrawals by each of the partners must always be equal.

_____   **4.** The partnership agreement should include the procedures for sharing profits and losses but should not include the investment of each partner.

_____   **5.** Noncash assets that are invested in the business are recorded at their current market value.

_____   **6.** Separate capital accounts are set up for each partner, but only one withdrawal account is used by all of the partners.

_____   **7.** Partners are not required to pay federal, state, or personal income taxes on their share of the business's net income.

_____   **8.** If a specific method for dividing net income or net loss among the partners is not set out in the partnership agreement, then the law provides that the division shall be equal among the partners.

_____   **9.** The division of partnership profits and losses is usually based on the partners' contributions of services and capital.

_____   **10.** The owners' equity section of the balance sheet for a partnership is called the Capital section.

_____   **11.** When using the fractional-share basis, a partnership's net income or loss is divided equally among the partners.

Part 3 Analyzing Transactions for a Partnership (14 points)

Directions: Teresa Hardee and Gail Taylor, two high school seniors, have formed a partnership to operate a babysitting service. Analyze the transactions below to determine the account titles to be debited and credited. Use the following account titles.

A. Cash in Bank
B. Baby Care Supplies
C. Play Equipment

D. Teresa Hardee, Capital
E. Gail Taylor, Capital
F. Teresa Hardee, Withdrawals

G. Gail Taylor, Withdrawals
H. Income Summary

	Debit	Credit
0. Teresa Hardee invested cash, baby care supplies, and play equipment in the business.	A, B, C	D
1. Gail Taylor invested a slide in the business.		
2. Recorded an additional cash investment by each partner.		
3. Recorded a cash withdrawal by Teresa Hardee.		
4. Gail Taylor withdrew baby care supplies.		
5. Recorded the closing entry for the equal distribution of net income for each partner.		
6. Recorded the closing entry for closing the withdrawals account for Gail Taylor.		
7. Recorded the closing entry for closing the withdrawals account for Teresa Hardee.		

Part 4 Advantages and Disadvantages of Partnerships (8 points)

Directions: In the space provided below, indicate whether the statement expresses an advantage or a disadvantage of a partnership. Place an "A" in the space for an advantage or a "D" for a disadvantage.

Answer

A	**0.** Opportunity to bring together abilities, experiences, and resources
	1. Ease of formation
	2. Limited life of the partnership
	3. Decision making without formal meetings
	4. Shared responsibility for the decision of one of the partners
	5. Inability to transfer one partner's interest in the partnership without the consent of the other partners
	6. No levying of federal and state income taxes against the partnership
	7. Personal liability for the debts of the partnership
	8. Few legal restrictions

Exercise 26-1, Page 582

	Ratio	Fractions
1.	3:1	_____
2.	5:3:1	_____
3.	3:2:1:1	_____
4.	2:2:1	_____
5.	3:2	_____

Exercise 26-2, Page 583

			Share of Net Income	
	Net Income	Partner 1	Partner 2	Partner 3
1.	$45,000	_____	_____	
2.	$89,700	_____	_____	
3.	$22,000	_____	_____	
4.	$32,000	_____	_____	_____
5.	$92,700	_____	_____	_____

Problem 26-1, Page 583

GENERAL JOURNAL   PAGE _____

	DATE	DESCRIPTION	POST. REF.	DEBIT	CREDIT	
1						1
2						2
3						3
4						4
5						5
6						6
7						7
8						8
9						9
10						10
11						11
12						12
13						13
14						14
15						15
16						16
17						17

Problem 26-2, Page 583

GENERAL JOURNAL

PAGE _____

	DATE	DESCRIPTION	POST. REF.	DEBIT	CREDIT	
1						1
2						2
3						3
4						4
5						5
6						6
7						7

Problem 26-3, Page 583

GENERAL JOURNAL

PAGE _____

	DATE	DESCRIPTION	POST. REF.	DEBIT	CREDIT	
1						1
2						2
3						3
4						4
5						5
6						6
7						7
8						8
9						9
10						10
11						11

GENERAL LEDGER (PARTIAL)

ACCOUNT _Barbara Scott, Capital_   ACCOUNT NO. _301_

DATE	EXPLANATION	POST. REF.	DEBIT	CREDIT	BALANCE DEBIT	BALANCE CREDIT
19-- Dec. 31	Balance	✔				67312 00

ACCOUNT _Barbara Scott, Withdrawals_   ACCOUNT NO. _305_

DATE	EXPLANATION	POST. REF.	DEBIT	CREDIT	BALANCE DEBIT	BALANCE CREDIT
19-- Dec. 31	Balance	✔			6600 00	

Problem 26-3, Page 583 (Concluded)

GENERAL LEDGER (PARTIAL)

ACCOUNT *Martin Towers, Capital*   ACCOUNT NO. **310**

DATE		EXPLANATION	POST. REF.	DEBIT	CREDIT	BALANCE DEBIT	BALANCE CREDIT
19-- Dec.	31	Balance	✓				49601 00

ACCOUNT *Martin Towers, Withdrawals*   ACCOUNT NO. **315**

DATE		EXPLANATION	POST. REF.	DEBIT	CREDIT	BALANCE DEBIT	BALANCE CREDIT
19-- Dec.	31	Balance	✓			5400 00	

ACCOUNT *Income Summary*   ACCOUNT NO. **320**

DATE		EXPLANATION	POST. REF.	DEBIT	CREDIT	BALANCE DEBIT	BALANCE CREDIT
19-- Dec.	31	Closing Entry	G13		49636 00		49636 00
	31	Closing Entry	G13	59336 00		9700 00	

Problem 26-4, Page 584

_____

_____

R & C
Work
For the Year Ended

	ACCT. NO.	ACCOUNT NAME	TRIAL BALANCE DEBIT	TRIAL BALANCE CREDIT	ADJUSTMENTS DEBIT	ADJUSTMENTS CREDIT
1	101	Cash in Bank	17928 00			
2	105	Accounts Receivable	4310 00			
3	110	Office Supplies	495 00			(a) 335 00
4	115	Roofing Supplies	15610 00			(b) 11470 00
5	120	Prepaid Insurance	2400 00			(c) 1200 00
6	150	Office Equipment	2650 00			
7	155	Accum. Depr.-Office Equip.		1016 00		(d) 185 00
8	160	Truck	19890 00			
9	165	Accum. Depr.-Truck		3100 00		(e) 3900 00
10	170	Building	30000 00			
11	175	Accum. Depr.-Building		3600 00		(f) 1200 00
12	180	Land	10000 00			
13	201	Accounts Payable		7945 00		
14	301	R. Lions, Capital		42238 00		
15	305	R. Lions, Withdrawals	8700 00			
16	310	C. Castle, Capital		17538 00		
17	315	C. Castle, Withdrawals	8100 00			
18	320	Income Summary				
19	401	Consulting Fees		15900 00		
20	405	Roofing Fees		62750 00		
21	501	Advertising Expense	2400 00			
22	505	Depr. Exp.-Office Equip.			(d) 185 00	
23	510	Depr. Exp.-Truck			(e) 3900 00	
24	515	Depr. Exp.-Building			(f) 1200 00	
25	520	Insurance Expense			(c) 1200 00	
26	525	Office Supplies Expense			(a) 335 00	
27	530	Roofing Supplies Expense			(b) 11470 00	
28	535	Salaries Expense	28109 00			
29	540	Truck Expense	1400 00			
30	545	Utilities Expense	2095 00			
31			154087 00	154087 00	18290 00	18290 00
32		Net Income				

Roofing
Sheet
December 31, 19--

ADJUSTED TRIAL BALANCE		INCOME STATEMENT		BALANCE SHEET		
DEBIT	CREDIT	DEBIT	CREDIT	DEBIT	CREDIT	
17928 00				17928 00		1
4310 00				4310 00		2
160 00				160 00		3
4140 00				4140 00		4
1200 00				1200 00		5
2650 00				2650 00		6
	1201 00				1201 00	7
19890 00				19890 00		8
	7000 00				7000 00	9
30000 00				30000 00		10
	4800 00				4800 00	11
10000 00				10000 00		12
	7945 00				7945 00	13
	42238 00				42238 00	14
8700 00				8700 00		15
	17538 00				17538 00	16
8100 00				8100 00		17
						18
	15900 00		15900 00			19
	62750 00		62750 00			20
2400 00		2400 00				21
185 00		185 00				22
3900 00		3900 00				23
1200 00		1200 00				24
1200 00		1200 00				25
335 00		335 00				26
11470 00		11470 00				27
28109 00		28109 00				28
1400 00		1400 00				29
2095 00		2095 00				30
159372 00	159372 00	52294 00	78650 00	107078 00	80722 00	31
		26356 00			26356 00	32
		78650 00	78650 00	107078 00	107078 00	33
						34
						35
						36
						37
						38

Problem 26-5, Page 584 (Continued)
(2)

Problem 26-5, Page 584 (Continued)
(4)

GENERAL JOURNAL   PAGE _____

	DATE	DESCRIPTION	POST. REF.	DEBIT	CREDIT	
1						1
2						2
3						3
4						4
5						5
6						6
7						7
8						8
9						9
10						10
11						11
12						12
13						13
14						14
15						15
16						16
17						17
18						18
19						19
20						20
21						21
22						22
23						23
24						24
25						25
26						26
27						27
28						28
29						29
30						30
31						31
32						32
33						33
34						34
35						35
36						36
37						37
38						38

Problem 26-5, Page 584 (Concluded)

GENERAL JOURNAL PAGE _____

	DATE	DESCRIPTION	POST. REF.	DEBIT	CREDIT	
1						1
2						2
3						3
4						4
5						5
6						6
7						7
8						8
9						9
10						10

Problem 26-6, Page 584

(1) O'Riley: _____

White: _____

Garrity: _____

(2) O'Riley: _____

White: _____

Garrity: _____

(3) O'Riley: _____

White: _____

Garrity: _____

Use this space for calculations.

27 Accounting for Corporations

Name _____

Date _____ Class _____

Total Points: 43   Student's Score _____

Part 1   Accounting Vocabulary (10 points)

Directions: Using terms from the following list, complete the sentences below. Write the letter of the term you have chosen in the space provided.

A. authorized capital stock
B. board of directors
C. closely held corporation
D. common stock
E. dividend

F. paid-in capital in excess of par
G. par value
H. preferred stock

I. proxy
J. publicly held corporation
K. statement of stockholders' equity

Answer

_____K_____   **0.** The financial statement that reports the changes that have taken place in all of the stockholders' equity accounts during the fiscal period is the __?__ .

_____   **1.** The maximum number of shares of stock that a corporation may issue is called its __?__ .

_____   **2.** The stock that has certain privileges over common stock is called __?__ .

_____   **3.** When a corporation issues only one type of stock, the stock is called __?__ .

_____   **4.** The stockholders' equity account that is used to record the sale of stock at higher than par value is the __?__ account.

_____   **5.** A corporation owned by a few persons or by a family and whose stock is not sold to the general public is called a(n) __?__ .

_____   **6.** A group who governs and is responsible for the affairs of the corporation is called a(n) __?__ .

_____   **7.** A __?__ is one whose stock is widely held, has a large market, and is traded on a stock exchange.

_____   **8.** __?__ is the amount assigned to each share of stock and printed as a dollar amount on the stock certificates.

_____   **9.** A __?__ is a return on the money invested by the stockholder.

_____   **10.** A document that gives the stockholder's voting rights to someone else when the stockholder cannot attend a stockholders' meeting is called a(n) __?__ .

Part 2   Analyzing Transactions for a Corporation (10 points)

Directions: Using the following account titles, analyze the transactions below. Determine the account(s) to be debited and credited. Write your answers in the space provided.

A. Cash in Bank
B. Common Stock
C. Dividends—Common

D. Dividends Payable—Common
E. Dividends Payable—Preferred
F. Dividends—Preferred

G. $5 Preferred Stock
H. Paid-in Capital in Excess of Par

	Debit	Credit
0. Issued 10,000 shares of common stock at $6 per share.	A	B
1. Issued 2,000 shares of $6 par common stock at $7.50 per share.	_____	_____
2. Declared a cash dividend of 85¢ per share on the 12,000 shares.	_____	_____
3. Issued a check for the payment of the dividend declared.	_____	_____
4. Issued 500 shares of $5 preferred stock, $100 par, at $100 per share.	_____	_____
5. Declared a cash dividend on the 500 shares of $5 preferred stock issued.	_____	_____

Part 3   Corporations (15 points)

Directions: Read each of the following statements to determine whether the statement is true or false. Write your answer in the space provided.

Answer

_____True_____   **0.** The Dividends account is increased on the debit side.

_____   **1.** An ownership certificate is proof of ownership in a corporation and lists the name of the stockholder, the number of shares issued, and the date they were issued.

_____   **2.** When a dividend is declared, the method used by all corporations is to debit the amount of the dividend directly into the Retained Earnings account.

_____   **3.** The stated dividend rate for preferred stock is an annual rate.

_____   **4.** Publicly held corporations cannot prepare a statement of retained earnings and must therefore prepare a statement of stockholders' equity.

_____   **5.** The common preference that preferred stockholders have is the right to receive dividends before they are paid to common stockholders.

_____   **6.** Even though a corporation is authorized to issue two types of stock, only one account is set up to record the two types of stock.

_____   **7.** Forming a corporation is less costly than forming a sole proprietorship or a partnership.

_____   **8.** Amounts that decrease account balances are enclosed in parentheses on the statement of stockholders' equity.

_____   **9.** The board of directors has the duty to hire professional managers to operate the corporation.

_____   **10.** Both the net income earned and the dividends declared by a corporation increase the Retained Earnings account.

_____   **11.** A privately held corporation is usually owned by a small family, and a publicly held corporation is usually owned by a very large family.

_____   **12.** There are more corporations than there are sole proprietorships and partnerships in the United States.

_____   **13.** A corporation may enter into contracts, borrow money, acquire property, and sue in the courts in the same manner as a person.

_____   **14.** The only types of information reported on a statement of stockholders' equity are the number of any shares of stock issued and the total amount received for those shares.

_____   **15.** The various organization costs incurred by a corporation when getting started include attorneys' fees for legal services and payments to promoters to sell stock.

Part 4   Advantages and Disadvantages of Corporations (8 points)

Directions: In the space provided below, indicate whether the statement expresses an advantage or a disadvantage of a corporation. Place an "A" in the space for an advantage or a "D" for a disadvantage.

Answer

_____D_____   **0.** Filing of numerous reports

_____   **1.** Limited liability of the owners

_____   **2.** Close regulation by state and federal governments

_____   **3.** Risk limited to individual investment

_____   **4.** Full disclosure to the public

_____   **5.** Sale of stock between stockholders without approval of other stockholders

_____   **6.** Double taxation of the corporation and the stockholders

_____   **7.** Continuous existence of the corporation

_____   **8.** Separate legal entity

Exercise 27-1, Page 603

(1) _____

_____

(2) _____

_____

(3) _____

_____

Exercise 27-2, Page 603

(1) _____

(2) _____

Exercise 27-3, Page 603

Transaction	Reported on Statement of Stockholders' Equity? (Yes/No)
1	
2	
3	
4	
5	
6	
7	
8	

Exercise 27-4, Page 603

(1) _____

(2) _____

(3) _____

Problem 27-1, Page 604

GENERAL JOURNAL

PAGE _____

	DATE		DESCRIPTION	POST. REF.	DEBIT	CREDIT	
1							1
2							2
3							3
4							4
5							5
6							6
7							7
8							8
9							9
10							10
11							11
12							12
13							13
14							14
15							15
16							16
17							17
18							18
19							19
20							20
21							21
22							22
23							23
24							24
25							25
26							26
27							27
28							28
29							29
30							30
31							31
32							32
33							33
34							34
35							35
36							36
37							37
38							38

Problem 27-2, Page 604

GENERAL JOURNAL

PAGE _____

	DATE	DESCRIPTION	POST. REF.	DEBIT	CREDIT	
1						1
2						2
3						3
4						4
5						5
6						6
7						7
8						8
9						9
10						10
11						11
12						12
13						13
14						14
15						15
16						16
17						17
18						18
19						19
20						20
21						21

GENERAL LEDGER (PARTIAL)

ACCOUNT _Cash in Bank_____ ACCOUNT NO. _101_

DATE	EXPLANATION	POST. REF.	DEBIT	CREDIT	BALANCE DEBIT	BALANCE CREDIT
Dec. 1	Balance	✓			98 650 00	

ACCOUNT _Dividends Payable - Preferred_____ ACCOUNT NO. _220_

DATE	EXPLANATION	POST. REF.	DEBIT	CREDIT	BALANCE DEBIT	BALANCE CREDIT

GENERAL LEDGER (PARTIAL)

ACCOUNT *Dividends Payable - Common*   ACCOUNT NO. 225

DATE	EXPLANATION	POST. REF.	DEBIT	CREDIT	BALANCE DEBIT	BALANCE CREDIT

ACCOUNT *Retained Earnings*   ACCOUNT NO. 310

DATE	EXPLANATION	POST. REF.	DEBIT	CREDIT	BALANCE DEBIT	BALANCE CREDIT
19-- Jan. 1	Balance	✓				169 014 00

ACCOUNT *Dividends - Preferred*   ACCOUNT NO. 315

DATE	EXPLANATION	POST. REF.	DEBIT	CREDIT	BALANCE DEBIT	BALANCE CREDIT

ACCOUNT *Dividends - Common*   ACCOUNT NO. 320

DATE	EXPLANATION	POST. REF.	DEBIT	CREDIT	BALANCE DEBIT	BALANCE CREDIT

ACCOUNT *Income Summary*   ACCOUNT NO. 325

DATE	EXPLANATION	POST. REF.	DEBIT	CREDIT	BALANCE DEBIT	BALANCE CREDIT
19-- Dec. 31	Closing Entry	G14		879 562 00		879 562 00
31	Closing Entry	G14	744 562 00			135 000 00

Problem 27-3, Page 605

GENERAL JOURNAL

PAGE _____

	DATE	DESCRIPTION	POST. REF.	DEBIT	CREDIT	
1						1
2						2
3						3
4						4
5						5
6						6
7						7
8						8
9						9
10						10
11						11
12						12
13						13
14						14
15						15
16						16
17						17
18						18
19						19
20						20
21						21
22						22
23						23
24						24
25						25
26						26
27						27
28						28
29						29
30						30
31						31
32						32
33						33
34						34
35						35
36						36
37						37
38						38

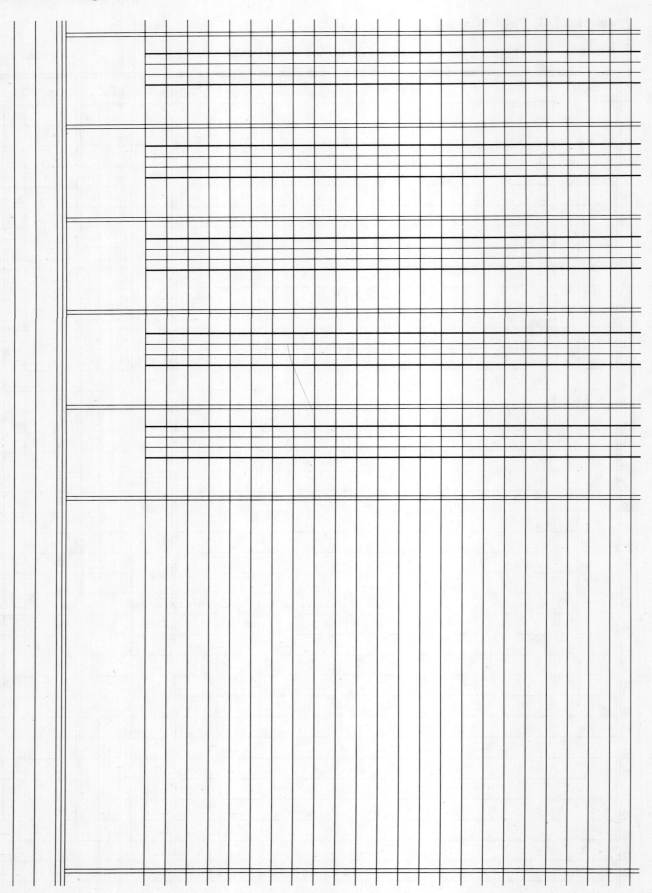

Problem 27-5, Page 605

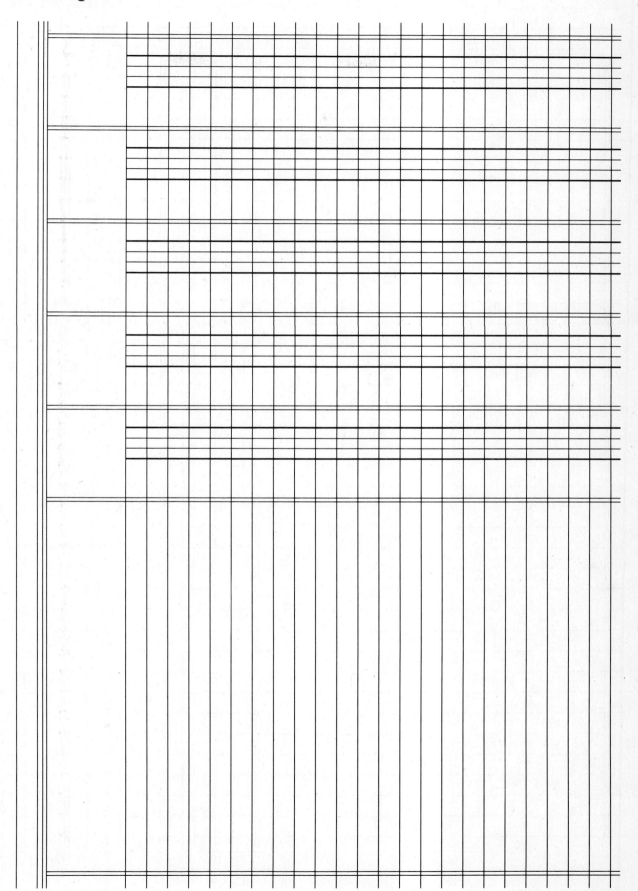

Problem 27-6, Page 606
(1)

GENERAL JOURNAL

	DATE	DESCRIPTION	POST. REF.	DEBIT	CREDIT	
1						1
2						2
3						3
4						4
5						5
6						6
7						7
8						8
9						9
10						10
11						11
12						12
13						13
14						14
15						15
16						16
17						17
18						18
19						19
20						20
21						21
22						22
23						23
24						24
25						25
26						26
27						27
28						28
29						29
30						30
31						31
32						32
33						33
34						34
35						35
36						36
37						37
38						38

Name _____

Date _____ Class _____

Total Points: 50   Student's Score _____

Part 1   Accounting Vocabulary (18 points)

Directions: Using terms from the following list, complete the sentences below. Write the letter of the term you have chosen in the space provided.

A. administrative expenses
B. base year
C. comparability
D. current liabilities
E. current ratio
F. full disclosure
G. horizontal analysis

H. investments
I. liquidity ratio
J. long-term liabilities
K. materiality
L. profitability ratios
M. quick ratio

N. ratio analysis
O. relevance
P. reliability
Q. selling expenses
R. vertical analysis
S. working capital

Answer

_____D_____   **0.** __?__ are debts that are expected to be paid within the next accounting period.

_____   **1.** Assets that are not intended to be converted to cash or to be used in the normal operations of the business within the next accounting period are called __?__ .

_____   **2.** The accounting guideline that requires that anyone preparing a financial report include enough information so that the report is complete is referred to as __?__ .

_____   **3.** __?__ is the amount by which current assets exceed current liabilities.

_____   **4.** __?__ are used to evaluate the earnings performance of a business during an accounting period.

_____   **5.** __?__ is the accounting guideline that states that relatively important data are included in financial reports.

_____   **6.** Each dollar amount reported on a financial statement is also stated as a percentage of a base amount reported on the same statement when using __?__ .

_____   **7.** The __?__ is a measure of the relationship between short-term liquid assets and current liabilities.

_____   **8.** __?__ relates to the confidence users have in the financial information provided by accountants for the purpose of making informed business decisions.

_____   **9.** Debts that are not required to be paid within the next accounting period are referred to as __?__ .

_____   **10.** A(n) __?__ is a measure of a business's ability to pay its current debts as they become due and to provide for unexpected needs of cash.

_____   **11.** The __?__ is the relationship between current assets and current liabilities.

_____   **12.** Costs related to the management of the business are referred to as __?__ .

_____   **13.** __?__ is a comparison of two items on a financial statement, which results in a percentage used to evaluate the relationship between the two items.

_____   **14.** __?__ are incurred to sell or market the merchandise or services sold by a business.

_____   **15.** __?__ means that the information contained on financial statements makes a difference to a user in reaching a decision about a business.

_____   **16.** A year that is used for comparison is called the __?__ .

_____   **17.** __?__ is the comparison of the same items on financial statements for two or more accounting periods and the analysis of changes from one period to the next.

_____   **18.** __?__ refers to accounting information that can be compared from one fiscal period to another or from one business to another.

Part 2   Analyzing and Interpreting Financial Statements (16 points)

Directions: Read each of the following statements to determine whether the statement is true or false. Write your answer in the space provided.

Answer

_____True_____ **0.** Operating expenses are the cash spent, assets consumed, or liabilities incurred to earn revenue for a business.

_____ **1.** The three qualitative characteristics of accounting are relevance, reliability, and conservatism.

_____ **2.** Examples of selling expenses are insurance expense and salaries of managers.

_____ **3.** Return on common stockholders' equity is one ratio that looks at profitability from the point of view of the investor.

_____ **4.** Working capital, the current ratio, and the quick ratio are common liquidity measures.

_____ **5.** The current ratio is calculated by dividing the dollar amount of current assets by the dollar amount of current expenses.

_____ **6.** Financial statements are more difficult to analyze if they are classified.

_____ **7.** Interest paid and interest earned are examples of revenue and expenses that do not result from the normal operations of a business.

_____ **8.** Vertical analysis uses the percentage of increase or decrease from one period to the next for each amount on the financial statement.

_____ **9.** A limitation of the current ratio is that it is based on total current assets.

_____ **10.** A current ratio of 1:1 or lower is considered favorable by creditors.

_____ **11.** Accounts Receivable is not used to compute the quick ratio.

_____ **12.** On a balance sheet arranged for vertical analysis, each asset amount is expressed as a percentage of total assets.

_____ **13.** Full disclosure and materiality are two guidelines that accountants follow when preparing financial reports.

_____ **14.** Dollar amounts are usually more useful than percentages in analyzing financial statements.

_____ **15.** To compare the separate operating expenses of a business from one period to the next, expenses are usually classified by liquidity.

_____ **16.** The financial statements issued by a business may be used by managers, investors, creditors, and unions.

Part 3   Classifying Financial Statements (16 points)

Directions: Using the following codes, indicate in which section of the financial statements each of the account titles below would appear. Write your answer in the space provided.

CA Current Assets
I Investments
P Property, Plant, and Equipment
CL Current Liabilities

LTL Long-Term Liabilities
STE Stockholders' Equity
R Revenue
CMS Cost of Merchandise Sold

SE Selling Expenses
AE Administrative Expenses
OE Other Expenses
OR Other Revenue

Answer

_____CA_____ **0.** Cash in Bank

_____ **1.** Merchandise Inventory, Dec. 1, 19 —

_____ **2.** Land

_____ **3.** Interest Income

_____ **4.** Office Salaries Expense

_____ **5.** Mortgage Payable

_____ **6.** Sales

_____ **7.** Merchandise Inventory, Jan. 1, 19 —

_____ **8.** Building

_____ **9.** JMK, Inc. (stock)

_____ **10.** Accounts Payable

_____ **11.** Advertising Expense

_____ **12.** Interest Expense

_____ **13.** Accounts Receivable

_____ **14.** Common Stock

_____ **15.** Purchases

_____ **16.** Retained Earnings

Exercise 28-1, Page 624

	1992	1991	Amount of Increase (Decrease)	Percentage of Increase (Decrease)
Current Assets	$540,000	$510,000	$ _____	_____
Property, Plant, and Equip.	455,000	470,000	_____	_____
Total Assets	$995,000	$980,000	_____	_____
Liabilities	$410,000	$400,000	_____	_____
Stockholders' Equity	585,000	580,000	_____	_____
Total Liabilities and Stockholders' Equity	$995,000	$980,000	$ _____	_____

Exercise 28-2, Page 625

	1992		1991	
	Dollars	Percentage	Dollars	Percentage
Net Sales	$700,000	_____	$625,000	_____
Cost of Merchandise Sold	450,000	_____	380,000	_____
Gross Profit on Sales	250,000	_____	245,000	_____
Operating Expenses	175,000	_____	175,000	_____
Net Income	$ 75,000	_____	$ 70,000	_____

Exercise 28-3, Page 625

1. Working capital: _____

2. Current ratio: _____

3. Quick ratio: _____

Exercise 28-4, Page 625

	1992	1991
1. Return on common stockholders' equity	_____	_____
2. Return on sales	_____	_____

Problem 28-2, Page 626

Mini-Sports Shop, Inc.
Comparative Income Statement
For the Years Ended August 31, 1992 and 1991

	1992	1991	Increase (Decrease) (1992 over 1991) Dollars	Percentage
Revenue:				
Sales	$232,345	$208,578	$	
Less: Sales Ret. & Allow.	4,350	3,988		
Net Sales	227,995	204,590		
Cost of Merchandise Sold	135,678	122,345		
Gross Profit on Sales	92,317	82,245		
Operating Expenses:				
Selling Expenses:				
Advertising Expense	9,500	8,700		
Delivery Expense	7,678	7,456		
Depr. Exp.—Store Equip.	1,000	1,000		
Sales Salaries Expense	21,500	19,899		
Travel Expense	4,567	4,134		
Total Selling Expenses	44,245	41,189		
Administrative Expenses:				
Bad Debts Expense	2,350	2,200		
Depr. Exp.—Off. Equip.	2,000	2,000		
Insurance Expense	2,500	2,400		
Miscellaneous Expense	2,367	2,200		
Office Salaries Expense	12,345	11,397		
Rent Expense	5,000	4,500		
Total Admin. Expenses	26,562	24,697		
Total Operating Expenses	70,807	65,886		
Operating Income	21,510	16,359		
Other Revenue	4,500	1,550		
Other Expenses	270	456		
Net Income	$ 25,740	$ 17,453	$	

Mini-Sports Shop, Inc.
Comparative Balance Sheet
August 31, 1992 and 1991

	1992		1991	
	Dollars	**Percentage**	**Dollars**	**Percentage**
Assets				
Current Assets:				
Cash in Bank	$ 11,900	_____	$ 10,890	_____
Accounts Receivable (net)	16,780	_____	15,450	_____
Merchandise Inventory	45,000	_____	38,700	_____
Prepaid Expenses	2,100	_____	1,860	_____
Total Current Assets	75,780	_____	66,900	_____
Investments:				
Runner, Inc. (stock)	10,500	_____	8,500	_____
Property, Plant, and Equipment:				
Equipment (net)	35,000	_____	30,000	_____
Building (net)	75,000	_____	80,000	_____
Land	15,000	_____	15,000	_____
Total Property, Plant, and Equipment	125,000	_____	125,000	_____
Total Assets	$211,280	_____	$200,400	_____
Liabilities				
Current Liabilities:				
Notes Payable	$ 22,500	_____	$ 18,600	_____
Accounts Payable	15,600	_____	13,200	_____
Sales Tax Payable	1,300	_____	1,200	_____
Total Current Liabilities	39,400	_____	33,000	_____
Long-Term Liabilities:				
Mortgage Payable	15,000	_____	25,000	_____
Total Liabilities	54,400	_____	58,000	_____
Stockholders' Equity				
Capital Stock, $100 par, 5,000 shares authorized, 500 shares issued	50,000	_____	50,000	_____
Retained Earnings	106,880	_____	92,400	_____
Total Stockholders' Equity	156,880	_____	142,400	_____
Total Liabilities and Stockholders' Equity	$211,280	_____	$200,400	_____

Problem 28-4, Page 627
(1)

Working capital: _____

Current ratio: _____

Quick ratio: _____

(2)

Transaction	Working Capital	Current Ratio	Quick Ratio
1			
2			
3			
4			
5			
6			
7			
8			
9			
10			

Problem 28-5, Page 628

Eastway Metal Company
Balance Sheet
December 31, 19—

Cash in Bank	$ _____		Current Liabilities	$ _____
Merchandise Inventory	_____		Long-Term Liabilities	225,000
Property, Plant and Equipment	_____		Stockholders' Equity	_____
Total Assets	$ 500,000		Total Liabilities and Stockholders' Equity	$ 500,000

Eastway Metal Company
Income Statement
For the Year Ended December 31, 19—

Net Sales	$ _____
Cost of Merchandise Sold	_____
Gross Profit on Sales	_____
Total Operating Expenses	_____
Net Income	$ 10,500

Problem 28-6, Page 628

Bay State Lumber, Inc. Comparative Income Statement For the Years Ended December 31, 1992 and 1991				
			Increase (Decrease) 1992 over 1991	
	1992	1991	Dollars	Percentage
Net Sales	$690,106		$116,966	
Cost of Merchandise Sold		$281,834	59,028	
Gross Profit on Sales	349,244			19.9%
Total Operating Expenses		176,085		7.7%
Operating Income	159,601	115,221		
Other Revenue	1,802		197	
Other Expenses		1,403		(39.5%)
Net Income				

Additional Reinforcement Problems, Problem 2A, Page 631

| Transaction | ASSETS | | | | | = | LIABILITIES | + | OWNER'S EQUITY |
	Cash in Bank	Accts. Rec.	Office Supp.	Comp. Equip.	Office Equip.	=	Accounts Payable	+	Ashley Moore, Capital
1									
Balance						=		+	
2									
Balance						=		+	
3									
Balance						=		+	
4									
Balance						=		+	
5									
Balance						=		+	
6									
Balance						=		+	
7									
Balance						=		+	
8									
Balance						=		+	
9									
Balance						=		+	
10									
Balance						=		+	

(4) Sum of debit balances: _____

(5) Sum of credit balances: _____

Additional Reinforcement Problems, Problem 4A, Page 632

Account Title	Debit Balances	Credit Balances
	$	$
Totals	$	$

GENERAL JOURNAL

PAGE _____

	DATE	DESCRIPTION	POST. REF.	DEBIT	CREDIT	
1						1
2						2
3						3
4						4
5						5
6						6
7						7
8						8
9						9
10						10
11						11
12						12
13						13
14						14
15						15
16						16
17						17
18						18
19						19
20						20
21						21
22						22
23						23
24						24
25						25
26						26
27						27
28						28
29						29
30						30
31						31
32						32
33						33
34						34
35						35
36						36
37						37
38						38

Additional Reinforcement Problems, Problem 6A, Page 633

GENERAL JOURNAL   PAGE ___1___

	DATE	DESCRIPTION	POST. REF.	DEBIT	CREDIT	
1	19-- May 2	Cash in Bank		45000 00		1
2		Bruno Ciani, Capital			45000 00	2
3		Memo. 1				3
4	2	Rent Expense		750 00		4
5		Cash in Bank			750 00	5
6		Check 101				6
7	3	Dental Equipment		6500 00		7
8		Accts. Pay. - Health Co, Inc.			6500 00	8
9		Invoice 0063				9
10	5	Dental Supplies		900 00		10
11		Cash in Bank			900 00	11
12		Check 102				12
13	7	Office Furniture		2400 00		13
14		Cash in Bank			2400 00	14
15		Check 103				15
16	9	Accounts Receivable - Paula Mathis		400 00		16
17		Dental Fees			400 00	17
18		Invoice 101				18
19	15	Office Furniture		600 00		19
20		Bruno Ciani, Capital			600 00	20
21		Memo. 2				21
22	18	Cash in Bank		825 00		22
23		Dental Fees			825 00	23
24		Receipt 101				24
25	24	Accounts Payable - Health Co, Inc.		1000 00		25
26		Cash in Bank			1000 00	26
27		Check 104				27
28	26	Cash in Bank		100 00		28
29		Accts. Rec. - Paula Mathis			100 00	29
30		Receipt 102				30
31	28	Bruno Ciani, Withdrawals		500 00		31
32		Cash in Bank			500 00	32
33		Check 105				33
34	30	Utilities Expense		105 00		34
35		Cash in Bank			105 00	35
36		Check 106				36
37						37
38						38

GENERAL LEDGER

ACCOUNT _Cash in Bank_   ACCOUNT NO. 101

DATE	EXPLANATION	POST. REF.	DEBIT	CREDIT	BALANCE	
					DEBIT	CREDIT

ACCOUNT _Accounts Receivable – Paula Mathis_   ACCOUNT NO. 105

DATE	EXPLANATION	POST. REF.	DEBIT	CREDIT	BALANCE	
					DEBIT	CREDIT

ACCOUNT _Dental Supplies_   ACCOUNT NO. 110

DATE	EXPLANATION	POST. REF.	DEBIT	CREDIT	BALANCE	
					DEBIT	CREDIT

ACCOUNT _Dental Equipment_   ACCOUNT NO. 120

DATE	EXPLANATION	POST. REF.	DEBIT	CREDIT	BALANCE	
					DEBIT	CREDIT

ACCOUNT _Office Furniture_   ACCOUNT NO. 125

DATE	EXPLANATION	POST. REF.	DEBIT	CREDIT	BALANCE	
					DEBIT	CREDIT

Additional Reinforcement Problems, Problem 6A, Page 633 (Continued)

GENERAL LEDGER

ACCOUNT _Accounts Payable – Health Co, Inc._ ACCOUNT NO. _201_

DATE	EXPLANATION	POST. REF.	DEBIT	CREDIT	BALANCE DEBIT	BALANCE CREDIT

ACCOUNT _Bruno Ciani, Capital_ ACCOUNT NO. _301_

DATE	EXPLANATION	POST. REF.	DEBIT	CREDIT	BALANCE DEBIT	BALANCE CREDIT

ACCOUNT _Bruno Ciani, Withdrawals_ ACCOUNT NO. _305_

DATE	EXPLANATION	POST. REF.	DEBIT	CREDIT	BALANCE DEBIT	BALANCE CREDIT

ACCOUNT _Income Summary_ ACCOUNT NO. _310_

DATE	EXPLANATION	POST. REF.	DEBIT	CREDIT	BALANCE DEBIT	BALANCE CREDIT

ACCOUNT _Dental Fees_ ACCOUNT NO. _401_

DATE	EXPLANATION	POST. REF.	DEBIT	CREDIT	BALANCE DEBIT	BALANCE CREDIT

GENERAL LEDGER

ACCOUNT _Rent Expense_   ACCOUNT NO. _520_

DATE	EXPLANATION	POST. REF.	DEBIT	CREDIT	BALANCE DEBIT	BALANCE CREDIT

ACCOUNT _Utilities Expense_   ACCOUNT NO. _530_

DATE	EXPLANATION	POST. REF.	DEBIT	CREDIT	BALANCE DEBIT	BALANCE CREDIT

Additional Reinforcement Problems, Problem 7A, Page 634

ACCT. NO.	ACCOUNT NAME	TRIAL BALANCE DEBIT	TRIAL BALANCE CREDIT	INCOME STATEMENT DEBIT	INCOME STATEMENT CREDIT	BALANCE SHEET DEBIT	BALANCE SHEET CREDIT
1							
2							
3							
4							
5							
6							
7							
8							
9							
10							
11							
12							
13							
14							
15							
16							
17							
18							
19							
20							
21							
22							
23							
24							
25							
26							

(1)

(2)

Additional Reinforcement Problems, Problem 8A, Page 634 (Concluded)
(3)

GENERAL JOURNAL

PAGE _____

	DATE		DESCRIPTION	POST. REF.	DEBIT	CREDIT	
1							1
2							2
3							3
4							4
5							5
6							6
7							7
8							8
9							9
10							10
11							11
12							12
13							13
14							14
15							15
16							16
17							17
18							18
19							19
20							20
21							21
22							22
23							23
24							24
25							25
26							26
27							27
28							28
29							29
30							30
31							31
32							32
33							33
34							34
35							35
36							36
37							37
38							38

Additional Reinforcement Problems, Problem 10A, Page 635

(1)

		DOLLARS	CENTS
	$ _____ __ No. 1272		
	DATE _____ 19 _____		
	TO _____		
	FOR _____		
BAL. BRO. FWD.		13,462	96
ADD DEPOSITS			
TOTAL			
LESS THIS CHECK			
BAL. CARR. FWD.			

(2)

BANK RECONCILIATION FORM

PLEASE EXAMINE YOUR STATEMENT AT ONCE. ANY DISCREPANCY SHOULD BE REPORTED TO THE BANK IMMEDIATELY.

1. Record any transactions appearing on this statement but not listed in your checkbook.

2. List any checks still outstanding in the space provided to the right.

3. Enter the balance shown on this statement here.

4. Enter deposits recorded in your checkbook but not shown on this statement.

5. Total Lines 3 and 4 and enter here.

6. Enter total checks outstanding here.

7. Subtract Line 6 from Line 5. This adjusted bank balance should agree with your checkbook balance.

CHECKS OUTSTANDING		
Number	Amount	
TOTAL		

GENERAL JOURNAL

PAGE _____

	DATE	DESCRIPTION	POST. REF.	DEBIT	CREDIT	
1						1
2						2
3						3
4						4
5						5
6						6
7						7
8						8
9						9
10						10
11						11
12						12
13						13
14						14
15						15
16						16
17						17
18						18

GENERAL LEDGER (PARTIAL)

ACCOUNT *Cash in Bank* ACCOUNT NO. __101__

DATE	EXPLANATION	POST. REF.	DEBIT	CREDIT	BALANCE DEBIT	BALANCE CREDIT
19-- Apr. 30	Balance	✓			1346296	

ACCOUNT *Miscellaneous Expense* ACCOUNT NO. __520__

DATE	EXPLANATION	POST. REF.	DEBIT	CREDIT	BALANCE DEBIT	BALANCE CREDIT
19-- Apr. 30	Balance	✓			61047	

Additional Reinforcement Problems, Problem 11A, Page 635

SALES JOURNAL

PAGE _____

	DATE	SALES SLIP NO.	CUSTOMER'S ACCOUNT DEBITED	POST. REF.	SALES CREDIT	SALES TAX PAYABLE CREDIT	ACCOUNTS RECEIVABLE DEBIT	
1								1
2								2
3								3
4								4
5								5
6								6
7								7
8								8
9								9
10								10
11								11
12								12
13								13
14								14
15								15
16								16
17								17
18								18
19								19
20								20
21								21
22								22
23								23
24								24
25								25
26								26
27								27
28								28
29								29
30								30
31								31
32								32
33								33
34								34
35								35
36								36
37								37

PAGE _____

CASH RECEIPTS JOURNAL

DATE	DOC. NO.	ACCOUNT TITLE	POST. REF.	GENERAL CREDIT	SALES CREDIT	SALES TAX PAYABLE CREDIT	ACCOUNTS RECEIVABLE CREDIT	SALES DISCOUNTS DEBIT	CASH IN BANK DEBIT
1									
2									
3									
4									
5									
6									
7									
8									
9									
10									
11									
12									
13									
14									
15									
16									
17									
18									
19									
20									
21									
22									
23									
24									
25									
26									
27									
28									

Additional Reinforcement Problems, Problem 12A, Page 636 (Concluded)

ACCOUNTS RECEIVABLE SUBSIDIARY LEDGER

Name *Kathy Curley*

Address *86 Wellesley Avenue, Ann Arbor, MI 48104*

DATE	EXPLANATION	POST. REF.	DEBIT	CREDIT	BALANCE
19-- Aug. 1	Balance	✓			420 24

Name *Robert Gaudet*

Address *5 Keane Road, Ann Arbor, MI 48103*

DATE	EXPLANATION	POST. REF.	DEBIT	CREDIT	BALANCE
19-- Aug. 1	Balance	✓			156 20

Name *Julie Murphy*

Address *5 Billow Street, Ann Arbor, MI 48105*

DATE	EXPLANATION	POST. REF.	DEBIT	CREDIT	BALANCE
19-- Aug. 1	Balance	✓			1 066 54

Name *Richard Stratton*

Address *30 Orchard Circle, Ann Arbor, MI 48103*

DATE	EXPLANATION	POST. REF.	DEBIT	CREDIT	BALANCE
19-- Aug. 1	Balance	✓			306 67

PURCHASES JOURNAL

PAGE ___

DATE	INVOICE NO.	CREDITOR'S ACCOUNT CREDITED	POST. REF.	ACCOUNTS PAYABLE CREDIT	PURCHASES DEBIT	ACCOUNT DEBITED	POST. REF.	DEBIT

GENERAL

GENERAL LEDGER (PARTIAL)

ACCOUNT *Supplies*   ACCOUNT NO. _120_

DATE		EXPLANATION	POST. REF.	DEBIT	CREDIT	BALANCE DEBIT	BALANCE CREDIT
19-- Oct.	1	Balance	✓			725 50	

ACCOUNT *Store Equipment*   ACCOUNT NO. _150_

DATE		EXPLANATION	POST. REF.	DEBIT	CREDIT	BALANCE DEBIT	BALANCE CREDIT
19-- Oct.	1	Balance	✓			9 416 00	

ACCOUNT *Accounts Payable*   ACCOUNT NO. _201_

DATE		EXPLANATION	POST. REF.	DEBIT	CREDIT	BALANCE DEBIT	BALANCE CREDIT
19-- Oct.	1	Balance	✓				2 030 65

ACCOUNT *Purchases*   ACCOUNT NO. _501_

DATE		EXPLANATION	POST. REF.	DEBIT	CREDIT	BALANCE DEBIT	BALANCE CREDIT
19-- Oct.	1	Balance	✓			29 694 16	

CASH PAYMENTS JOURNAL

PAGE _____

DATE	DOC. NO.	ACCOUNT TITLE	POST. REF.	GENERAL DEBIT	ACCOUNTS PAYABLE DEBIT	PURCHASES DISCOUNTS CREDIT	CASH IN BANK CREDIT	
								1
								2
								3
								4
								5
								6
								7
								8
								9
								10
								11
								12
								13
								14
								15
								16
								17
								18
								19
								20
								21
								22
								23
								24
								25
								26
								27
								28

Additional Reinforcement Problems, Problem 14A, Page 637 (Continued)

ACCOUNTS PAYABLE SUBSIDIARY LEDGER

Name *Bugatti Leather Works*

Address *2800 Erie Avenue, Lorain, OH 44052*

DATE		EXPLANATION	POST. REF.	DEBIT	CREDIT	BALANCE
19-- Nov.	1	Balance	✓			2 1 9 0 00

Name *Curry Leather Co.*

Address *2190 Rodman Road, Fayetteville, AR 72701*

DATE		EXPLANATION	POST. REF.	DEBIT	CREDIT	BALANCE
19-- Nov.	1	Balance	✓			9 0 0 00

Name *Harris Luggage Co.*

Address *416 Hennepin Avenue, Minneapolis, MN 55414*

DATE		EXPLANATION	POST. REF.	DEBIT	CREDIT	BALANCE
19-- Nov.	1	Balance	✓			2 3 0 0 00

Name *Kenwood Manufacturing*

Address *1600 Roosevelt Highway, Kendall, NY 14476*

DATE		EXPLANATION	POST. REF.	DEBIT	CREDIT	BALANCE
19-- Nov.	1	Balance	✓			2 2 5 5 55

ACCOUNTS PAYABLE SUBSIDIARY LEDGER

Name _Renaissance Leather_

Address _3300 Timberlake Road, Knoxville, TN 37920_

DATE		EXPLANATION	POST. REF.	DEBIT	CREDIT	BALANCE
19-- Nov.	1	Balance	✓			2561 00

GENERAL LEDGER (PARTIAL)

ACCOUNT _Accounts Payable_   ACCOUNT NO. _201_

DATE		EXPLANATION	POST. REF.	DEBIT	CREDIT	BALANCE DEBIT	BALANCE CREDIT
19-- Nov.	1	Balance	✓				10206 55

Additional Reinforcement Problems, Problem 15A, Page 638

GENERAL JOURNAL

PAGE _____

	DATE	DESCRIPTION	POST. REF.	DEBIT	CREDIT	
1						1
2						2
3						3
4						4
5						5
6						6
7						7
8						8
9						9
10						10
11						11
12						12
13						13
14						14
15						15
16						16
17						17
18						18

Additional Reinforcement Problems, Problem 15B, Page 638

1. _____

_____

2. _____

_____

3. _____

_____

_____

_____

4. _____

_____

5. _____

_____

	ACCT. NO.	ACCOUNT NAME	TRIAL BALANCE		ADJUSTMENTS	
			DEBIT	CREDIT	DEBIT	CREDIT
1	101	Cash in Bank				
2	105	Accounts Receivable				
3	110	Merchandise Inventory				
4	115	Supplies				
5	120	Prepaid Insurance				
6	150	Office Equipment				
7	155	Store Equipment				
8	201	Accounts Payable				
9	205	Fed. Inc. Tax Payable				
10	210	Sales Tax Payable				
11	301	Capital Stock				
12	305	Retained Earnings				
13	310	Income Summary				
14	401	Sales				
15	405	Sales Returns & Allow.				
16	501	Purchases				
17	505	Transportation In				
18	510	Purchases Discounts				
19	601	Advertising Expense				
20	605	Insurance Expense				
21	610	Miscellaneous Expense				
22	615	Rent Expense				
23	620	Salaries Expense				
24	625	Supplies Expense				
25	630	Fed. Inc. Tax Expense				
26						
27						
28						
29						
30						
31						
32						
33						
34						
35						
36						
37						
38						

ADJUSTED TRIAL BALANCE		INCOME STATEMENT		BALANCE SHEET		
DEBIT	CREDIT	DEBIT	CREDIT	DEBIT	CREDIT	
						1
						2
						3
						4
						5
						6
						7
						8
						9
						10
						11
						12
						13
						14
						15
						16
						17
						18
						19
						20
						21
						22
						23
						24
						25
						26
						27
						28
						29
						30
						31
						32
						33
						34
						35
						36
						37
						38

Darnell Hobby
Work
For the Year Ended

	ACCT. NO.	ACCOUNT NAME	TRIAL BALANCE DEBIT	TRIAL BALANCE CREDIT	ADJUSTMENTS DEBIT	ADJUSTMENTS CREDIT
1	101	Cash in Bank	1206174			
2	105	Accounts Receivable	169310			
3	110	Merchandise Inventory	3746216			(a) 364971
4	115	Supplies	308590			(b) 194207
5	120	Prepaid Insurance	486000			(c) 162000
6	125	Office Equipment	1164700			
7	130	Store Equipment	2659300			
8	201	Accounts Payable		345942		
9	205	Fed. Inc. Tax Payable				(d) 21800
10	210	Sales Tax Payable		57988		
11	301	Capital Stock		2000000		
12	305	Retained Earnings		4027121		
13	310	Income Summary			(a) 364971	
14	401	Sales		17396258		
15	405	Sales Discounts	139170			
16	410	Sales Returns & Allow.	304435			
17	501	Purchases	6216150			
18	505	Transportation In	310805			
19	510	Purchases Discounts		124323		
20	515	Purchases Returns & Allow.		155404		
21	601	Advertising Expense	168000			
22	605	Bank Card Fees Expense	81376			
23	610	Insurance Expense			(c) 162000	
24	615	Miscellaneous Expense	40340			
25	620	Rent Expense	1200000			
26	625	Salaries Expense	5246600			
27	630	Supplies Expense			(b) 194207	
28	635	Utilities Expense	209870			
29	640	Fed. Inc. Tax Expense	450000		(d) 21800	
30			24107036	24107036	742978	742978
31		Net Income				
32						
33						
34						
35						
36						
37						
38						

& Crafts Center, Inc.
Sheet
June 30, 19--

ADJUSTED TRIAL BALANCE		INCOME STATEMENT		BALANCE SHEET		
DEBIT	CREDIT	DEBIT	CREDIT	DEBIT	CREDIT	
1206174				1206174		1
169310				169310		2
3381245				3381245		3
114383				114383		4
324000				324000		5
1164700				1164700		6
2659300				2659300		7
	345942				345942	8
	21800				21800	9
	57988				57988	10
	2000000				2000000	11
	4027121				4027121	12
364971		364971				13
	17396258		17396258			14
139170		139170				15
304435		304435				16
6216150		6216150				17
310805		310805				18
	124323		124323			19
	155404		155404			20
168000		168000				21
81376		81376				22
162000		162000				23
40340		40340				24
1200000		1200000				25
5246600		5246600				26
194207		194207				27
209870		209870				28
471800		471800				29
24128836	24128836	15109724	17675985	9019112	6452851	30
		2566261			2566261	31
		17675985	17675985	9019112	9019112	32
						33
						34
						35
						36
						37
						38

Additional Reinforcement Problems, Problem 17A, Page 640 (Concluded)

(2)

(3)

Additional Reinforcement Problems ■ 471

Additional Reinforcement Problems, Problem 18A, Page 640

GENERAL JOURNAL

PAGE _____

	DATE	DESCRIPTION	POST. REF.	DEBIT	CREDIT	
1						1
2						2
3						3
4						4
5						5
6						6
7						7
8						8
9						9
10						10
11						11

Additional Reinforcement Problems, Problem 18B, Page 640

GENERAL JOURNAL

PAGE _____

	DATE	DESCRIPTION	POST. REF.	DEBIT	CREDIT	
1						1
2						2
3						3
4						4
5						5
6						6
7						7
8						8
9						9
10						10
11						11
12						12
13						13
14						14
15						15
16						16
17						17
18						18
19						19
20						20
21						21
22						22
23						23

Name_____ Date_____ Class_____

Additional Reinforcement Problems, Problem 19A, Page 641

PAYROLL REGISTER

PAY PERIOD ENDING_____ 19____ DATE OF PAYMENT_____

EMPLOYEE NUMBER	NAME	MAR. STATUS	EXEMP.	TOTAL HOURS	RATE	EARNINGS			DEDUCTIONS							NET PAY	CK. NO.
						REGULAR	OVERTIME	TOTAL	SOC. SEC. TAX	MED. TAX	FED. INC. TAX	STATE INC. TAX	HOSP. INS.	OTHER	TOTAL		
1																	
2																	
3																	
4																	
5																	
6																	
7																	
8																	
9																	
10																	
11																	
12																	
13																	
14																	
15																	
16																	
17																	
18																	
19																	
20																	
21																	
22																	
23																	
24																	
25																	
	TOTALS																

Other Deductions: Write the appropriate code letter to the left of the amount: B—U.S. Savings Bonds; C—Credit Union; UD—Union Dues; UW—United Way.

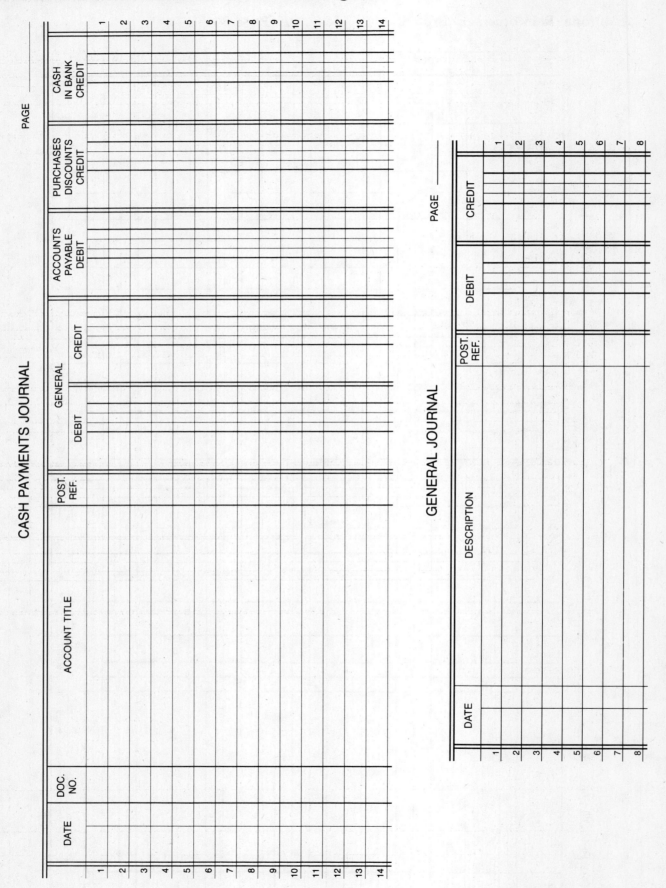

CASH PAYMENTS JOURNAL

GENERAL JOURNAL

Additional Reinforcement Problems, Problem 21A, Page 642

PETTY CASH REGISTER

PAGE ____

DATE	VOU. NO.	EXPLANATION	PAYMENTS	OFFICE SUPPLIES	DELIVERY EXPENSE	MISC. EXPENSE	GENERAL ACCOUNT TITLE	AMOUNT
1								
2								
3								
4								
5								
6								
7								
8								
9								
10								
11								
12								
13								
14								
15								
16								
17								
18								
19								
20								
21								
22								
23								
24								
25								
26								
27								
28								

DISTRIBUTION OF PAYMENTS

(1)

Date	Cost	Annual Depreciation	Accumulated Depreciation	Book Value
Oct. 12, 1991				
Dec. 31, 1991				
Dec. 31, 1992				
Dec. 31, 1993				
Dec. 31, 1994				

(2)

GENERAL JOURNAL   PAGE _____

	DATE	DESCRIPTION	POST. REF.	DEBIT	CREDIT	
1						1
2						2
3						3
4						4
5						5
6						6
7						7
8						8
9						9
10						10
11						11

GENERAL LEDGER (PARTIAL)

ACCOUNT _Delivery Truck_   ACCOUNT NO. _150_

DATE	EXPLANATION	POST. REF.	DEBIT	CREDIT	BALANCE DEBIT	BALANCE CREDIT

ACCOUNT _Accumulated Depreciation – Delivery Truck_   ACCOUNT NO. _155_

DATE	EXPLANATION	POST. REF.	DEBIT	CREDIT	BALANCE DEBIT	BALANCE CREDIT

Additional Reinforcement Problems, Problem 23A, Page 643

(1)

Estimate of uncollectible accounts: _____

(2)

GENERAL JOURNAL

PAGE _____

	DATE	DESCRIPTION	POST. REF.	DEBIT	CREDIT	
1						1
2						2
3						3
4						4
5						5
6						6

(3)

GENERAL LEDGER (PARTIAL)

ACCOUNT _Allowance for Uncollectible Accounts_   ACCOUNT NO. 110

DATE	EXPLANATION	POST. REF.	DEBIT	CREDIT	BALANCE DEBIT	BALANCE CREDIT
19-- Dec. 31	Balance	✓				1 060 50

ACCOUNT _Bad Debts Expense_   ACCOUNT NO. 605

DATE	EXPLANATION	POST. REF.	DEBIT	CREDIT	BALANCE DEBIT	BALANCE CREDIT

(4)

Book value of accounts receivable: _____

(1)

	Specific Identification Method	Fifo Method	Lifo Method	Weighted Average Cost Method
Ending Inventory	$ _____	$ _____	$ _____	$ _____

(2)

Specific Identification Method:

Total items available for sale (_____ units) $ _____

Less ending inventory (_____ units)   _____

Cost of merchandise sold (_____ units) $ _____

Fifo Method:

Total items available for sale (_____ units) $ _____

Less ending inventory (_____ units)   _____

Cost of merchandise sold (_____ units) $ _____

Lifo Method:

Total items available for sale (_____ units) $ _____

Less ending inventory (_____ units)   _____

Cost of merchandise sold (_____ units) $ _____

Weighted Average Cost Method:

Total items available for sale (_____ units) $ _____

Less ending inventory (_____ units)   _____

Cost of merchandise sold (_____ units) $ _____

Additional Reinforcement Problems, Problem 25A, Page 644

CASH RECEIPTS JOURNAL

PAGE _____

DATE	DOC. NO.	ACCOUNT TITLE	POST. REF.	GENERAL DEBIT	GENERAL CREDIT	SALES CREDIT	SALES TAX PAYABLE CREDIT	ACCOUNTS RECEIVABLE CREDIT	CASH IN BANK DEBIT
									1
									2
									3
									4
									5
									6
									7
									8
									9
									10
									11

CASH PAYMENTS JOURNAL

PAGE _____

DATE	DOC. NO.	ACCOUNT TITLE	POST. REF.	GENERAL DEBIT	GENERAL CREDIT	ACCOUNTS PAYABLE DEBIT	PURCHASES DISCOUNTS CREDIT	CASH IN BANK CREDIT
								1
								2
								3
								4
								5
								6
								7
								8
								9
								10
								11

GENERAL JOURNAL

PAGE _____

	DATE		DESCRIPTION	POST. REF.	DEBIT	CREDIT	
1							1
2							2
3							3
4							4
5							5
6							6
7							7
8							8
9							9
10							10
11							11
12							12
13							13
14							14
15							15
16							16
17							17
18							18
19							19
20							20
21							21
22							22
23							23
24							24
25							25
26							26
27							27
28							28
29							29
30							30
31							31
32							32
33							33
34							34
35							35
36							36
37							37
38							38

Additional Reinforcement Problems, Problem 26A, Page 644

GENERAL JOURNAL

PAGE _____

	DATE	DESCRIPTION	POST. REF.	DEBIT	CREDIT	
1						1
2						2
3						3
4						4
5						5
6						6
7						7
8						8
9						9
10						10
11						11

Additional Reinforcement Problems, Problem 26B, Page 644

GENERAL JOURNAL

PAGE _____

	DATE	DESCRIPTION	POST. REF.	DEBIT	CREDIT	
1						1
2						2
3						3
4						4
5						5
6						6
7						7
8						8
9						9
10						10
11						11

GENERAL LEDGER (PARTIAL)

ACCOUNT *Susan Keith, Capital*   ACCOUNT NO. *301*

DATE	EXPLANATION	POST. REF.	DEBIT	CREDIT	BALANCE DEBIT	BALANCE CREDIT
19-- Dec. 31	Balance	✓				75 0 0 0 00

GENERAL LEDGER (PARTIAL)

ACCOUNT *Susan Keith, Withdrawals* ACCOUNT NO. 305

DATE		EXPLANATION	POST. REF.	DEBIT	CREDIT	BALANCE DEBIT	BALANCE CREDIT
19-- Dec.	31	Balance	✓			7500 00	

ACCOUNT *Mike Yonan, Capital* ACCOUNT NO. 310

DATE		EXPLANATION	POST. REF.	DEBIT	CREDIT	BALANCE DEBIT	BALANCE CREDIT
19-- Dec.	31	Balance	✓				8500 00

ACCOUNT *Mike Yonan, Withdrawals* ACCOUNT NO. 315

DATE		EXPLANATION	POST. REF.	DEBIT	CREDIT	BALANCE DEBIT	BALANCE CREDIT
19-- Dec.	31	Balance	✓			4800 00	

ACCOUNT *Income Summary* ACCOUNT NO. 320

DATE		EXPLANATION	POST. REF.	DEBIT	CREDIT	BALANCE DEBIT	BALANCE CREDIT
19-- Dec.	31	Closing Entry	G11				2750 00

(3)

Additional Reinforcement Problems, Problem 27A, Page 645

GENERAL JOURNAL

PAGE _____

	DATE		DESCRIPTION	POST. REF.	DEBIT	CREDIT	
1							1
2							2
3							3
4							4
5							5
6							6
7							7
8							8
9							9
10							10
11							11
12							12
13							13
14							14
15							15
16							16
17							17
18							18
19							19
20							20
21							21
22							22
23							23
24							24
25							25
26							26
27							27
28							28
29							29
30							30
31							31
32							32
33							33
34							34
35							35
36							36
37							37
38							38

Additional Reinforcement Problems, Problem 28A, Page 646

Wonderland Toys, Inc.
Comparative Income Statement
For the Years Ended August 31, 1992 and 1991

	1992	1991	Increase (Decrease) (1992 over 1991) Dollars	Percentage
Revenue:				
Sales	$243,576	$219,326	$	
Less: Sales Ret. & Allowances	3,450	4,566		
Net Sales	240,126	214,760		
Cost of Merchandise Sold	143,579	126,784		
Gross Profit on Sales	96,547	87,976		
Operating Expenses:				
Selling Expenses:				
Advertising Expense	8,700	7,600		
Delivery Expense	8,674	8,796		
Depr. Exp. — Store Equip.	1,500	1,200		
Sales Salaries Expense	23,400	20,120		
Travel Expense	5,342	4,123		
Total Selling Expenses	47,616	41,839		
Administrative Expenses:				
Bad Debts Expense	2,250	2,320		
Depr. Exp. — Office Equip.	1,550	1,575		
Insurance Expense	1,500	2,355		
Office Salaries Expense	13,635	12,345		
Rent Expense	4,000	5,000		
Supplies Expense	3,245	2,100		
Total Admin. Expenses	26,180	25,695		
Total Operating Expenses	73,796	67,534		
Operating Income	22,751	20,442		
Other Income	3,000	2,550		
Other Expenses	280	355		
Net Income	$ 25,471	$ 22,637	$	

Wonderland Toys, Inc.
Comparative Balance Sheet
August 31, 1992 and 1991

	1992		1991	
	Dollars	**Percentage**	**Dollars**	**Percentage**
Assets				
Current Assets:				
Cash in Bank	$ 12,790		$ 11,900	
Accounts Receivable (net)	14,567		16,890	
Merchandise Inventory	38,500		35,000	
Prepaid Expenses	2,300		1,900	
Total Current Assets	68,157		65,690	
Investments:				
Runner, Inc. (stock)	12,500		10,500	
Property, Plant, and Equipment:				
Equipment (net)	40,000		45,000	
Building (net)	80,000		85,000	
Land	15,000		15,000	
Total Property, Plant, and Equipment	135,000		145,000	
Total Assets	$215,657		$221,190	
Liabilities				
Current Liabilities:				
Notes Payable	$ 27,600		$ 22,600	
Accounts Payable	24,500		15,000	
Sales Tax Payable	1,200		890	
Total Current Liabilities	53,300		38,490	
Long-Term Liabilities:				
Mortgage Payable	20,000		30,000	
Total Liabilities	73,300		68,490	
Stockholders' Equity				
Common Stock, $10 par, 25,000 shares authorized, 5,000 shares issued	50,000		50,000	
Retained Earnings	92,357		102,700	
Total Stockholders' Equity	142,357		152,700	
Total Liabilities and Stockholders' Equity	$215,657		$221,190	

Enrichment Chapter A, Recording Transactions in the Combination Journal, Exercise 1, Page 652

Date	Transaction	General Dr.	General Cr.	Accounts Receivable Dr.	Accounts Receivable Cr.	Sales Cr.	Sales Tax Pay-able Cr.	Accounts Payable Dr.	Accounts Payable Cr.	Pur-chases Dr.	Cash in Bank Dr.	Cash in Bank Cr.
1	Debit	√										
	Credit								√			
2	Debit											
	Credit											
5	Debit											
	Credit											
8	Debit											
	Credit											
10	Debit											
	Credit											
13	Debit											
	Credit											
15	Debit											
	Credit											
18	Debit											
	Credit											
22	Debit											
	Credit											
25	Debit											
	Credit											
25	Debit											
	Credit											
30	Debit											
	Credit											
31	Debit											
	Credit											
31	Debit											
	Credit											

COMBINATION

	DATE		ACCOUNT TITLE	DOC. NO.	POST. REF.	GENERAL		ACCOUNTS RECEIVABLE	
						DEBIT	CREDIT	DEBIT	CREDIT
1									
2									
3									
4									
5									
6									
7									
8									
9									
10									
11									
12									
13									
14									
15									
16									
17									
18									
19									
20									
21									
22									
23									
24									
25									
26									
27									
28									
29									
30									
31									
32									
33									
34									

JOURNAL

PAGE _____

MEDICAL FEES CREDIT	LABORATORY FEES CREDIT	ACCOUNTS PAYABLE		MEDICAL SUPPLIES DEBIT	CASH IN BANK		
		DEBIT	CREDIT		DEBIT	CREDIT	
							1
							2
							3
							4
							5
							6
							7
							8
							9
							10
							11
							12
							13
							14
							15
							16
							17
							18
							19
							20
							21
							22
							23
							24
							25
							26
							27
							28
							29
							30
							31
							32
							33
							34

COMBINATION

	DATE		ACCOUNT TITLE	DOC. NO.	POST. REF.	GENERAL		ACCOUNTS RECEIVABLE	
						DEBIT	CREDIT	DEBIT	CREDIT
1									
2									
3									
4									
5									
6									
7									
8									
9									
10									
11									
12									
13									
14									
15									
16									
17									
18									
19									
20									
21									
22									
23									
24									
25									
26									
27									
28									
29									
30									
31									
32									
33									
34									
35									
36									

490 ■ Enrichment Chapter A

JOURNAL

PAGE _____

SALES CREDIT	SALES TAX PAYABLE CREDIT	ACCOUNTS PAYABLE		PURCHASES DEBIT	CASH IN BANK		
		DEBIT	CREDIT		DEBIT	CREDIT	
							1
							2
							3
							4
							5
							6
							7
							8
							9
							10
							11
							12
							13
							14
							15
							16
							17
							18
							19
							20
							21
							22
							23
							24
							25
							26
							27
							28
							29
							30
							31
							32
							33
							34
							35
							36

COMBINATION

	DATE		ACCOUNT TITLE	DOC. NO.	POST. REF.	GENERAL		ACCOUNTS RECEIVABLE	
						DEBIT	CREDIT	DEBIT	CREDIT
1									
2									
3									
4									
5									
6									
7									
8									
9									
10									
11									
12									
13									
14									
15									
16									
17									
18									
19									
20									
21									
22									
23									
24									
25									
26									
27									
28									
29									
30									
31									
32									
33									
34									

Enrichment Chapter B, The Accrual Basis of Accounting, Exercise 1, Page 662

Item	Prepaid Expense	Unearned Revenue	Accrued Expense	Accrued Revenue
1	√			
2				
3				
4				
5				
6				
7				
8				
9				
10				

Enrichment Chapter B, Problem 1, Page 662

GENERAL JOURNAL

PAGE _____

	DATE	DESCRIPTION	POST. REF.	DEBIT	CREDIT	
1						1
2						2
3						3
4						4
5						5
6						6
7						7
8						8
9						9
10						10
11						11
12						12
13						13
14						14
15						15
16						16
17						17
18						18

GENERAL JOURNAL

PAGE _____

	DATE		DESCRIPTION	POST. REF.	DEBIT	CREDIT	
1							1
2							2
3							3
4							4
5							5
6							6
7							7
8							8
9							9
10							10
11							11
12							12
13							13
14							14
15							15
16							16
17							17
18							18
19							19
20							20
21							21
22							22
23							23
24							24
25							25
26							26
27							27
28							28
29							29
30							30
31							31
32							32
33							33
34							34
35							35
36							36
37							37
38							38

Appendix A   Using a Ten-Key Numeric Keypad

Ten-key numeric keypads are found on electronic calculators and microcomputer keyboards. When you are keying quantities of numerical data, your ability to input numbers by touch will make your task easier and faster.

Key Locations

The ten-key numeric keypad is usually arranged into four rows of three keys. The locations of the 1 to 9 keys are the same on all equipment. The locations of the 0 (zero), decimal, and enter keys—as well as other function keys—vary depending on the equipment. The following illustrations show some typical arrangements.

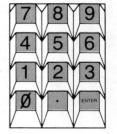

Home Position

On the ten-key numeric keypad, the 4–5–6 keys are called the **home keys**. These keys are the "starting point" from which you will operate the other number keys. The index finger of your right hand should rest on the 4 key, your middle finger on the 5 key, and your ring finger on the 6 key. Most keypads have a special "help" on the home keys so you can easily locate them: there may be a raised dot on the 5 key or the surfaces of the 4–5–6 keys may be concave (indented).

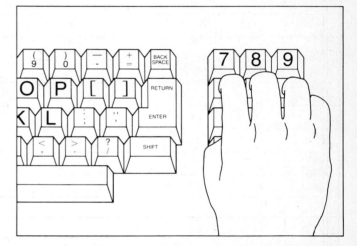

From the home keys, you reach up or down to tap other keys. The index finger is also used for the 7 and 1 keys. The middle finger is used for the 8 and 2 keys. The ring finger is used for the 9 and 3 keys.

The fingers used for the 0 (zero), decimal, and enter keys depend on the arrangement of the keypad. On some keypads, the thumb is used to tap the 0 (zero) key and the ring finger for the decimal key. The enter key on a microcomputer may be operated by the little finger or the thumb, depending on its location. On an electronic calculator, numbers are entered by using function keys: plus ($+$), minus ($-$), multiply ($\times$), divide ($\div$), and so on. The fingers used to operate these keys depend on the keys' location on the keyboard. Locate these keys on your keypad and determine the correct fingers to use to operate them.

Entering Numbers by Touch

Throughout the remaining pages of this appendix, you will learn to locate and operate the ten-key numeric keypad by touch. That is, you will enter numbers on the keypad without looking at your fingers.

Your practice materials consist of columns of numbers. If you are using an electronic calculator, tap the plus ($+$) key after you have entered a number in a column. After entering all the numbers in a column, tap the equals ($=$) key. If you are using a microcomputer, tap the enter key after you have entered a number in a column. This will force a line break; each time you strike the enter key, the cursor will move to the next line. After entering all the numbers in a column, tap the enter key *twice* to leave extra space between the columns of numbers.

You will not be totaling these columns of numbers. You are learning now to enter numbers by touch, not how to add a column of figures. Also, if you are using a microcomputer, a special software program must be used if the numbers are to be added.

Using the 4–5–6 Keys

1. Locate the 4–5–6 keys (the home keys) on your keypad. Also locate the enter key if you're using a microcomputer or the plus key if you're using a calculator.
2. Place your index finger on the 4 key, your middle finger on the 5 key, and your ring finger on the 6 key.
3. To enter a number, tap the number keys, one at a time, in the same order as you read the digits from left to right. Always keep your fingers on the home keys.
4. When you have entered the last digit, tap the enter key (microcomputer) or the plus key (calculator).
5. Using the following problems, practice entering columns of numbers. Practice at a comfortable pace until you feel confident about each key's location.
6. After entering all of the numbers in a column, tap the enter key twice (microcomputer) or tap the equals key once (calculator).

1.	2.	3.	4.	5.	6.
444	555	666	456	554	664
555	666	454	654	445	445
666	444	545	465	564	566
456	654	446	556	664	645
564	546	646	656	565	465
646	465	546	465	655	654

7.	8.	9.	10.	11.	12.
456	564	646	555	666	444
654	546	465	666	454	545
446	646	546	456	654	465
556	656	465	554	445	564
664	565	655	664	466	566
645	465	654	444	555	666

13.	14.	15.	16.	17.	18.
654	666	464	666	456	555
546	546	656	654	454	545
456	546	656	654	454	545
465	646	546	555	446	454
444	654	654	556	445	456
555	564	546	554	444	654

19.	20.	21.	22.	23.	24.
5,655	4,556	456	55	445	6,656
45	645	4,564	4	56	4,655
6	54	655	54	6,664	566
456	46	4,545	5,554	465	465
664	564	5,664	564	5,644	64
56	5	65	445	56	544

Name _____ Date _____ Class _____

Using the 1, 7, and 0 Keys

1. Locate the 1, 7, and 0 (zero) keys on your keypad.
2. Place your fingers on the home keys.
3. Practice the reach from the home keys to each new key. Reach down to the 1 key and up to the 7 key with your index finger. Be sure to return your finger to the home keys after tapping the 1 and 7 keys. Strike the 0 (zero) key with your thumb.
4. Using the following problems, practice entering columns of numbers containing the new keys. Practice at a comfortable pace until you feel confident about each key's location. Be sure to keep your fingers in home-key position.

1.	2.	3.	4.	5.	6.
444	014	140	107	011	141
471	107	701	074	170	117
174	740	701	104	710	417
741	101	704	007	004	047
710	114	471	411	471	104
407	441	117	047	174	114

7.	8.	9.	10.	11.	12.
741	710	407	014	147	740
101	114	441	140	701	701
704	471	117	107	074	104
007	411	017	011	170	710
004	471	174	141	117	417
047	104	114	444	471	174

13.	14.	15.	16.	17.	18.
170	140	104	111	777	410
701	147	107	147	111	140
107	014	401	174	444	014
741	041	701	741	714	741
147	074	101	710	741	471
410	047	010	410	704	147

19.	20.	21.	22.	23.	24.
1,044	456	145	17	101	1,404
540	4,540	6,147	7,100	47	40
7,055	74	567	1,105	1,075	140
607	415	10	574	157	1,714
4,441	510	106	177	7,775	1,570
17	1,750	1,045	50	147	1,104

Using the 3 and 9 Keys

1. Locate the 3 and 9 keys on your keypad.
2. Place your fingers on the home keys.
3. Practice the reach from the home keys to each new key. Reach down to the 3 key and up to the 9 key with your ring finger. Be sure to return your finger to the home keys after tapping the 3 and 9 keys.
4. Using the following problems, practice entering columns of numbers containing the new keys. Practice at a comfortable pace until you feel confident about each key's location. Be sure to keep your fingers in home-key position.

7	8	9
4	5	6
1	2	3
Ø	.	ENTER

1.	2.	3.	4.	5.	6.
666	669	339	966	939	699
999	663	363	393	363	936
333	936	336	966	393	939
963	396	936	633	639	336
639	936	636	393	369	696
399	363	996	993	369	939

7.	8.	9.	10.	11.	12.
963	639	399	669	663	936
396	936	363	339	363	336
936	636	993	966	393	966
633	393	993	939	363	393
639	369	369	699	936	939
336	696	939	666	999	333

13.	14.	15.	16.	17.	18.
369	333	963	639	669	339
396	666	369	963	663	336
393	999	639	936	636	933
696	369	396	966	363	699
693	963	393	939	939	633
639	639	693	333	393	399

19.	20.	21.	22.	23.	24.
416	19	165	1,497	1,975	6,914
6,069	7,035	1,913	313	961	351
976	1,346	6	7,643	93	177
1,515	507	19	491	4,149	6,543
109	1,397	1,016	16	4,973	46
3,419	737	409	3,499	549	347

Using the 2 and 8 Keys

1. Locate the 2 and 8 keys on your keypad.
2. Place your fingers on the home keys.
3. Practice the reach from the home keys to each new key. Reach down to the 2 key and up to the 8 key with your middle finger. Be sure to return your finger to the home keys after tapping the 2 and 8 keys.
4. Using the following problems, practice entering columns of numbers containing the new keys. Practice at a comfortable pace until you feel confident about each key's location. Be sure to keep your fingers in home-key position.

1.	2.	3.	4.	5.	6.
555	228	885	285	582	828
888	852	285	258	558	825
222	522	825	525	582	852
582	252	588	858	825	258
822	528	258	582	525	885
522	855	852	825	582	282

7.	8.	9.	10.	11.	12.
582	822	522	228	852	522
252	528	855	885	285	825
588	258	258	285	825	525
858	582	825	582	558	582
825	525	582	828	528	852
852	885	282	555	888	222

13.	14.	15.	16.	17.	18.
888	585	222	828	522	228
222	522	555	825	852	822
852	555	888	852	285	825
258	582	258	258	852	828
582	258	852	885	825	258
528	282	528	282	558	522

19.	20.	21.	22.	23.	24.
498	8,650	3,907	670	4,323	83
2,889	61	778	7,494	3,362	4,428
5,268	201	9,165	9,726	565	733
102	1,750	319	50	975	10
2,500	850	90	586	64	4,953
20	796	9,594	13	1,456	684

Using the Decimal Key

1. Locate the decimal key on your keypad.
2. Place your fingers on the home keys.
3. Depending on the arrangement of keys on your numeric keypad, you may use your thumb, your middle finger, or your ring finger to tap the decimal key. Practice the reach from the home keys to the decimal key. Be sure to return your finger to the home keys after tapping the decimal key.
4. Using the following problems, practice entering columns of numbers containing the decimal key. Practice at a comfortable pace until you feel confident about the key's location. Be sure to keep your fingers in home-key position.

1.	2.	3.	4.	5.	6.
.777	.978	.998	8.78	7.88	8.79
.888	.987	.879	8.89	7.87	7.98
.999	.878	.787	8.87	8.97	9.89
.789	.987	.878	7.88	9.77	9.87
.897	.789	.797	9.87	7.97	7.89
.978	.797	.899	7.98	8.79	9.78

7.	8.	9.	10.	11.	12.
.456	.564	.654	6.54	6.45	4.66
.546	.645	.666	4.56	4.56	6.45
.546	.456	.654	5.46	6.45	4.65
.546	.555	.546	5.64	6.54	6.45
.655	.456	.465	4.46	5.64	5.56
.465	.656	.545	5.66	5.44	6.54

13.	14.	15.	16.	17.	18.
.111	.132	.231	2.21	3.31	2.23
.222	.213	.211	3.22	2.32	3.21
.333	.123	.223	3.12	1.33	1.22
.123	.213	.233	3.22	3.12	1.13
.321	.231	.321	2.12	1.23	3.12
.113	.111	.222	2.22	1.22	2.11

19.	20.	21.	22.	23.	24.
146.53	544.00	654.87	91.07	112.39	48.11
214.98	734.08	101.06	37.79	216.49	13.87
734.56	408.96	141.69	84.13	479.17	46.51
273.16	456.00	454.00	17.50	146.32	19.30
105.14	349.98	913.54	72.37	557.34	68.34
607.40	366.08	204.67	72.20	126.67	92.73

Practice entering the following columns of numbers by touch.

1.	**2.**	**3.**	**4.**	**5.**	**6.**
654	321	980	213	798	927
984	302	957	316	980	945
870	651	867	620	981	254
907	543	697	531	972	842
987	503	314	631	874	964
870	324	426	264	803	973

7.	**8.**	**9.**	**10.**	**11.**	**12.**
4,792	2,489	2,940	4,892	4,209	9,842
7,306	3,491	6,783	1,246	9,812	7,956
8,217	5,397	7,617	6,036	1,567	1,154
6,783	1,569	1,215	7,263	1,465	1,450
2,769	7,056	6,578	8,754	6,056	4,718
1,190	2,356	8,754	1,270	4,998	2,531

13.	**14.**	**15.**	**16.**	**17.**	**18.**
990	2,574	972	4,123	928	456
72	5	9,547	60	8,619	61
69	4,626	747	19	50	5,741
474	103	621	21	1	5,787
7,674	7	304	1,584	198	53
903	55	73	9,569	3	2,209

19.	**20.**	**21.**	**22.**	**23.**	**24.**
4.50	7.87	17.28	1.75	42.69	98.42
1.47	5.25	23.75	6.72	73.50	30.91
2.89	2.40	66.61	8.10	12.46	53.97
6.01	9.81	17.00	8.46	12.49	88.60
9.58	4.04	54.06	2.79	10.82	29.03
7.14	1.69	55.08	1.90	23.77	62.20

25.	**26.**	**27.**	**28.**	**29.**	**30.**
468.	48.2	.8	284.0	41.87	154.88
.489	2,537.	5,827.	100.	4,057.4	888.
214.2	852.	.024	8.45	89.45	.0082
7.12	3.978	18.73	56.0	2.25	200.08
6,394.4	257.0	85.00	23.00	20.0	632.48
.58	.2684	1.045	.89	36.248	64.1

31.	32.	33.	34.	35.	36.
6,880.62	97.41	43.75	6.60	41.15	68.02
3,507.05	600.92	42.67	.39	9.02	48.76
1,921.13	925.15	91.93	31.00	20.09	86.78
5,983.04	315.92	35.40	2.43	30.17	65.90
3,674.24	105.84	54.23	5.99	10.48	26.63
4,586.39	308.15	24.21	11.48	7.43	88.33

37.	38.	39.	40.	41.	42.
$ 267.14	$ 9.38	$ 162.50	$147.50	$ 38.95	$ 19.80
2,175.10	8,631.40	397.00	74.16	1,313.56	681.12
4,012.87	78.15	66.34	915.64	1,745.73	6,320.79
214.54	125.54	1,126.97	400.38	2,674.13	575.95
94.69	804.93	1,278.20	940.77	813.56	100.47
1,637.00	544.60	127.90	7.18	2.14	0.65

43.	44.	45.	46.	47.	48.
$ 9.95	$127.60	$ 5.45	$ 47.60	$ 92.60	$ 75.45
249.95	644.73	25.00	137.80	943.80	428.20
145.95	29.50	8.27	0.50	16.59	0.38
10.47	7.03	16.23	109.46	430.34	117.55
158.47	27.25	545.91	181.65	60.00	76.80
37.13	5.07	112.77	9.79	26.85	18.23

49.	50.	51.	52.	53.	54.
$ 655.20	$ 37.30	$ 250.30	$ 412.95	$ 740.65	$ 68.49
1,469.98	397.67	43.98	964.95	2,110.75	121.68
3,754.17	380.04	287.02	1,818.56	3,571.34	61.12
834.79	1,428.62	1,909.41	243.50	2,904.91	243.50
41.41	2,233.38	58.99	74.68	1,271.49	314.17
273.07	914.00	758.38	1,003.16	2,675.54	388.93

55.	56.	57.	58.	59.	60.
$ 61.93	$ 446.00	$ 20.67	$ 78.30	$ 519.02	$ 8.68
1,296.13	4,466.73	216.37	14.39	3,113.56	62.36
200.00	61.45	445.39	14.60	102.55	43.12
157.43	258.16	5,650.00	352.49	39.95	611.18
14.97	900.62	1,426.15	617.32	1,874.05	21.67
869.42	25.15	109.15	803.70	3,130.78	1,972.32

61.	62.	63.	64.	65.	66.
$ 267.50	$ 425.21	$ 1.25	$ 467.54	$ 65.27	$ 9.78
4.19	414.50	0.18	95.14	102.38	5.94
87.64	1,684.84	585.56	6,926.95	8,216.58	652.25
654.84	49.95	7.50	35.00	1,852.84	3,782.70
1,750.67	720.65	11.60	7.13	4.60	39.25
141.82	77.61	23.55	154.95	79.15	36.87